Practice in the Basic Skills Mathematics 5

Contents

Published by
CollinsEducational,
An imprint of HarperCollins*Publishers*
77–85 Fulham Palace Road, London W6 8JB
© 1978 D. Newton & D. Smith
0 00 318789 6
Printed by Martins The Printers Ltd., Berwick upon Tweed
Revised 1985
Reprinted 1987 (twice), 1989, 1990, 1991, 1992, 1993,
1994, 1995 (twice), 1996

Notation

A Write in   **a** figures   **b** words   the number shown on each abacus.

1 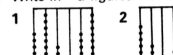   2   3   4 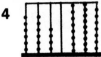   5

B Write in figures.

4 million	7 million	19 million	2 million	15 million
$\frac{1}{2}$ million	$\frac{1}{4}$ million	$\frac{3}{4}$ million	$\frac{1}{5}$ million	$\frac{1}{10}$ million
$3\frac{1}{4}$ million	$2\frac{3}{4}$ million	$6\frac{1}{2}$ million	$2\frac{3}{5}$ million	$4\frac{7}{10}$ million
0·1 million	0·4 million	0·7 million	0·2 million	0·6 million
3·3 million	2·5 million	1·8 million	3·4 million	6·9 million

C

	a	b	c
Add 10 to	a 402 341	b 160 592	c 999 999
Add 100 to	a 634 801	b 502 916	c 1 271 214
Add 10 000 to	a 437 216	b 50 439	c 207 986
Add 100 000 to	a 921 741	b 843 216	c 1 941 276
Add 1000 to	a 1 499 211	b 1 376 416	c 1 999 271

D Write the value in words of the underlined figures in each of these numbers.

435 261   2 431 276   909 214   54 251
297 616   1 627 401   808 531   756 394

E Write the number which is   **a** 1 less than   **b** 10 less than   **c** 100 less than each of these numbers.

$\frac{1}{2}$ million $\frac{1}{4}$ million $\frac{3}{4}$ million   300 000   350 000

4·2 million   2·1 million   8·3 million   470 000   610 000

Approximations

A Approximate these numbers to the nearest   **a** 10   **b** 100   **c** 1000.

54 729	13 269	202 435	60 987	120 696
444 909	38 451	899 823	54 163	914 429

B Approximate to the nearest   **a** hundredth   **b** tenth   **c** whole.

14·352	16·073	7·451	242·715	6·439
11·992	13·475	6·549	8·727	18·296

C Approximate to the nearest ten thousand.

429 000	516 214	1 421 216	801 216	34 921
1 427 500	350 001	2 069 350	609 215	414 916

D Approximate to the nearest million.

15 215 007	26 841 215	5 296 416	12 851 216
7 407 196	32 945 125	10 816 000	5 613 000

E Approximate to the nearest hundred thousand.

479 416	821 394	464 514	1 396 214	375 416
5 291 216	794 271	354 741	663 415	704 596

F Approximate to the nearest   **a** thousand   **b** ten thousand   **c** hundred thousand **d** million

5 416 299	14 767 345	4 636 921	12 392 906	7 439 899	12 930 914

Addition and subtraction

A Find

$156 + 40\,178 + \frac{1}{2}$ million $20\,476 + 296\,751 + 500\,279$

$6006 + 23\,745 + 927\,651$ $1 \cdot 4$ million $+ 35\,427 + 253\,651$

$35 + 471 + 969$ $2\frac{3}{4}$ million $+ 500\,000 + 62\,753$

$\frac{1}{4}$ million $+ 947 + 4299$ $10\,800 + 39 + 976$

$6 \cdot 7$ million $+ \frac{1}{2}$ million $+ 300\,000$ $35\,000 + 98\,000 + 202\,998$

B $\frac{3}{4}$ million $- 476\,296$ $217\,491 - 147\,281$

$3 \cdot 6$ million $- 2\,417\,399$ $500\,000 - \frac{1}{4}$ million

$247\,399 - 99\,541$ $3\,541\,000 - 2\,796\,395$

$1\,000\,005 - 868\,541$ $750\,000 - 0 \cdot 6$ million

$99\,000 - 87\,679$ $4\frac{3}{4}$ million $- 2 \cdot 7$ million

C **1** Find the total of two hundred and fifty thousand, $\frac{1}{2}$ million and seventeen thousand and sixty-six.

2 Find the difference between 431 621 and 808 471.

3 How much is $\frac{3}{4}$ million less than 943 541?

4 Find the sum of 42 714, 202 671, 5499 and 87.

5 How much greater than 492 741 is $\frac{1}{2}$ million?

6 43 216 plus 104 439 plus 99 549 plus 1 276 399.

7 1 439 992 subtract 953 899.

8 Twenty-four thousand minus sixteen thousand and nine.

9 Increase 4·7 million by 91 476.

10 Decrease 515 402 by 279 509.

11 1 435 629 plus 801 776 minus 927 598.

12 Take forty-one thousand nine hundred and fifty from the sum of three-quarters of a million and two hundred and fifty thousand and ninety-six.

Multiplication and division

A 1

435	2459	3216	926	6027
×8	×6	×11	×5	×7

2 4359 × 9   9091 × 4   29 361 × 3

B 375 × 10   426 × 10   1743 × 10   20 549 × 10

5271 × 30   694 × 70   4358 × 90   16 096 × 80

C

56	79	68	94	59	87
×16	×23	×54	×76	×17	×21

D

476	309	909	835	479	776
×32	×54	×27	×42	×67	×19

E 1075 × 13   1975 × 24   2461 × 92   8798 × 77

F 6⟌436   3⟌529   9⟌706   7⟌547   5⟌631   8⟌928

G 11⟌1271   7⟌2465   12⟌8325   9⟌7072   2⟌3546

H 12⟌20 171   6⟌53 542   4⟌67 541   8⟌25 372

I 16⟌96   31⟌87   15⟌59   23⟌93   13⟌47   21⟌63   27⟌82

J 19⟌132   29⟌257   21⟌189   32⟌305   28⟌267   36⟌354

K 17⟌294   33⟌825   16⟌751   22⟌683   35⟌937   27⟌541

L 18⟌1362   22⟌1541   51⟌1269   34⟌2515   19⟌1432

M 21⟌4240   17⟌3027   23⟌5632   18⟌7471   31⟌8415

N 4321 ÷ 26   1090 ÷ 25   3242 ÷ 35   6070 ÷ 15

Long multiplication

A 1 Multiply each number by **a** 10 **b** 30 **c** 50 **d** 80.

19 26 25 73 51 46 83 92 54 31

2 Multiply each number by **a** 100 **b** 400 **c** 700.

35 42 75 87 96 58 29 18 67 72

B 1

175	269	727	586	392	826
×100	×100	×100	×100	×100	×100

2

341	505	679	921	541	432
×700	×200	×500	×300	×400	×600

C

247	903	362	456	535	929
×150	×170	×180	×190	×160	×130

D

563	395	992	156	716	832
×210	×610	×810	×710	×510	×910

E

222	405	817	283	635	883
×520	×470	×630	×860	×950	×770

F

455	631	754	429	987	654
×301	×406	×603	×502	×804	×205

G

928	333	679	831	524	246
×419	×724	×632	×868	×953	×383

116	472	669	785	357	598
×628	×717	×434	×569	×342	×853

Long division — harder examples

A

$15\overline{)27\,416}$ $14\overline{)34\,327}$ $17\overline{)53\,416}$ $16\overline{)24\,137}$

$17\overline{)41\,206}$ $18\overline{)39\,502}$ $13\overline{)60\,271}$ $19\overline{)59\,328}$

B

$26\overline{)40\,321}$ $22\overline{)57\,621}$ $25\overline{)35\,471}$ $23\overline{)27\,909}$

$28\overline{)61\,342}$ $27\overline{)92\,147}$ $24\overline{)51\,151}$ $21\overline{)42\,106}$

C

$36\overline{)26\,329}$ $33\overline{)61\,112}$ $35\overline{)25\,324}$ $32\overline{)91\,351}$

$37\overline{)42\,151}$ $39\overline{)52\,001}$ $34\overline{)80\,191}$ $38\overline{)17\,629}$

D

$21\overline{)43\,152}$ $19\overline{)14\,351}$ $37\overline{)45\,161}$ $38\overline{)39\,124}$

$29\overline{)77\,321}$ $25\overline{)19\,720}$ $26\overline{)38\,262}$ $33\overline{)77\,066}$

E

$141\overline{)967}$ $115\overline{)627}$ $105\overline{)629}$ $123\overline{)767}$

F

$154\overline{)1025}$ $131\overline{)1246}$ $183\overline{)1064}$ $227\overline{)1946}$

G

$161\overline{)1815}$ $214\overline{)3416}$ $181\overline{)5621}$ $207\overline{)5152}$

H

$115\overline{)14\,767}$ $121\overline{)75\,403}$ $211\overline{)67\,693}$

$165\overline{)42\,600}$ $205\overline{)64\,251}$ $231\overline{)82\,196}$

I $4372 \div 16$ $5419 \div 21$ $20\,013 \div 33$

$42\,161 \div 35$ $20\,421 \div 133$ $6261 \div 26$

$4216 \div 111$ $9091 \div 38$ $14\,251 \div 23$

J   Divide

4161 by 18   7241 by 36 $18\,647 \div 116$

12 031 by 65   24 716 by 29 $20\,307 \div 47$

Decimals — notation

A Write the following vulgar fractions as decimals.

1 $\frac{12}{100}$ $\frac{3}{10}$ $\frac{17}{1000}$ $\frac{3}{1000}$ $\frac{7}{10}$ $\frac{9}{100}$ $\frac{9}{10}$ $\frac{71}{1000}$ $\frac{7}{100}$ $\frac{9}{1000}$

2 $\frac{3}{4}$ $\frac{13}{25}$ $\frac{7}{50}$ $\frac{19}{20}$ $\frac{1}{2}$ $\frac{13}{50}$ $\frac{7}{20}$ $\frac{11}{25}$ $\frac{17}{20}$ $\frac{1}{4}$

3 $4\frac{19}{1000}$ $6\frac{3}{25}$ $8\frac{9}{20}$ $1\frac{7}{10}$ $12\frac{3}{100}$ $10\frac{63}{1000}$ $2\frac{17}{25}$ $5\frac{3}{20}$

B How many thousandths in the following?

1   0·136   0·075   1·204   0·007   4·071   5·001   0·016   0·009

2 Put in a decimal point to make the 7 in each number worth 7 hundredths.

513 467   436 715   643 571   367 154   317 645

3 What is the 6 worth in each of the answers to question **2**?

4 Put in a decimal point to make the 5 in each number worth 5 thousandths.

132 415   32 651   96 205   200 531   25

5 What is the 2 worth in each of the answers to question **4**?

C Write out putting in the missing denominators.

1 $7\cdot38 = 7 + \frac{3}{} + \frac{8}{}$ $6\cdot027 = 6 + \frac{2}{} + \frac{7}{}$

   $12\cdot375 = 12 + \frac{3}{} + \frac{7}{} + \frac{5}{}$ $7\cdot102 = 7 + \frac{1}{} + \frac{2}{}$

2 Complete these statements with > or <.

0·18	0·6	2·017	2·008	4·17	0·417
0·03	0·027	0·167	0·2	0·076	0·009
1·06	1·057	46·167	46·176	0·6	0·36

Decimals — four rules

A $124 + 3.741 + 15.077$

$4.275 + 12\frac{7}{10} + 0.93$

$6\frac{7}{20} + 5.21 + 16.923$

$12\frac{1}{2} + 16 + 7.2 + 12.47$

$321.5 + 0.935 + 6.74$

$41.36 + 1.927 + 5\frac{6}{25}$

$1471.6 + 73.921 + 5.76$

$0.735 + 4.88 + 36.743$

$15\frac{7}{10} + 6\frac{3}{20} + 153.754$

$16.073 + 8.946 + 101.52$

B $144.337 - 93.946$

$2451.96 - 7.815$

$24\,560.6 - 43.257$

$27.679 - 8.489$

$6271 - 476.998$

$132.045 - 86.925$

$53\,416.1 - 7262.47$

$926.04 - 475.396$

$3611.3 - 594.009$

$20\,100.63 - 5714.29$

C 1 14.136×9 321.43×8 4.017×12 188.06×7

0.936×11 43.275×6 923.6×3 149.276×4

2 4321.06×5 1193.51×2 6251.2×12 5841.031×5

$20\,271.6 \times 11$ $32\,151.27 \times 4$ 9934.007×9 2116.27×8

3313.416×6 $22\,341.6 \times 7$ 5675.26×3 9354.9×2

D

$6\,|\,45.6$ $9\,|\,80.1$ $5\,|\,27.5$ $12\,|\,46.8$ $11\,|\,68.2$

$5\,|\,3.15$ $8\,|\,7.68$ $7\,|\,3.29$ $11\,|\,10.34$ $3\,|\,1.68$

$7\,|\,93.87$ $8\,|\,88.72$ $9\,|\,113.22$ $4\,|\,64.84$ $6\,|\,78.12$

$3\,|\,28.413$ $5\,|\,23.035$ $4\,|\,84.108$ $6\,|\,38.838$ $11\,|\,26.796$

Harder multiplication of decimals

A

0·56	0·73	0·61	0·39	0·79	0·86
×16	×41	×32	×29	×19	×36

0·19	0·28	0·47	0·92	0·66	0·83
×25	×37	×23	×18	×47	×18

B

1·72	15·45	23·09	2·66	5·27	16·73
×22	×21	×14	×25	×27	×15

13·25	7·45	11·92	21·47	9·32	12·09
×17	×28	×13	×18	×16	×19

C

4·27	11·43	6·21	9·46	14·66
×117	×103	×141	×212	×311

5·21	6·32	12·41	13·09	46·21
×106	×151	×111	×206	×231

D

0·57	0·61	0·93	0·47	0·82
×0·7	×0·9	×0·2	×0·6	×0·4

0·98	0·34	0·54	0·66	0·39
×0·8	×0·6	×0·5	×0·3	×0·7

E

12·45	15·26	22·19	32·46	27·35
×1·7	×2·7	×1·4	×2·9	×3·2

F

5·41	16·27	2·35	19·25	21·27
×13·5	×1·02	×14·3	×2·14	×8·71

G 1·27 × 0·9   32·41 × 3·6   7·49 × 2·41

11·41 × 13·2   0·96 × 0·17   10·46 × 3·09

Harder division of decimals

A

21)‾2·646‾   13)‾1·014‾   18)‾4·356‾   14)‾7·392‾   19)‾8·949‾

15)‾6·255‾   17)‾5·151‾   16)‾1·968‾   23)‾3·243‾   24)‾5·136‾

B

23)‾54·05‾   18)‾62·28‾   17)‾86·19‾   25)‾158·50‾   31)‾59·21‾

32)‾98·24‾   27)‾124·47‾   19)‾115·52‾   41)‾61·09‾   62)‾88·04‾

C

23)‾19·366‾   27)‾18·954‾   21)‾12·033‾   18)‾11·538‾   22)‾20·152‾

34)‾23·902‾   27)‾11·745‾   36)‾11·052‾   24)‾20·016‾   33)‾17·721‾

D

8)‾28·0‾   5)‾37·0‾   6)‾39·0‾   12)‾102·0‾   4)‾50·0‾   5)‾49·0‾

E

6)‾44·10‾   4)‾22·60‾   6)‾43·50‾   12)‾33·00‾   2)‾19·90‾   8)‾44·40‾

F

8)‾49·00‾   4)‾21·50‾   6)‾57·75‾   12)‾28·50‾   2)‾13·75‾   4)‾34·50‾

G

35)‾189·0‾   18)‾117·0‾   14)‾203·0‾   15)‾147·0‾   25)‾330·0‾

H

15)‾137·10‾   14)‾87·50‾   25)‾184·00‾   23)‾132·25‾   45)‾177·30‾

I

24)‾51·00‾   35)‾188·16‾   15)‾114·42‾   36)‾355·5‾   25)‾185·6‾

J

99·770 ÷ 22	238·7 ÷ 31	425·10 ÷ 26
117·6 ÷ 16	109·82 ÷ 34	370·00 ÷ 25
201·0 ÷ 15	47·355 ÷ 33	62·028 ÷ 18
196 ÷ 16	181·50 ÷ 25	690·90 ÷ 35
127·26 ÷ 21	181·35 ÷ 45	103·73 ÷ 23

K

260·78 ÷ 118	31·92 ÷ 105	11 087·6 ÷ 212
1044·0 ÷ 144	38·192 ÷ 112	1295·82 ÷ 207

Division by decimals

A

0·8) 0·52   0·4) 0·14   0·11) 0·0792   0·3) 0·177   0·5) 0·135

0·5) 0·17   0·12) 0·0156   0·7) 0·294   0·6) 0·042   0·9) 0·612

B

0·5) 2·630   0·8) 3·8   0·12) 0·7236   0·6) 5·562   0·3) 1·023

0·7) 2·086   0·11) 0·7799   0·9) 7·623   0·4) 2·50   0·12) 0·6408

C

0·4) 5·096   0·8) 11·400   0·9) 19·089   0·7) 23·863   0·6) 14·130

0·11) 1·9877   0·12) 3·8736   0·5) 1·2530   0·04) 0·6940   0·3) 3·921

D

1·3) 5·473   2·3) 6·187   0·16) 0·8464   2·5) 67·775   0·35) 8·3790

2·4) 34·128   0·15) 0·9360   1·9) 95·57   0·32) 0·6624   1·8) 2·646

E

1·3) 10·673   1·4) 13·230   0·15) 1·0980   2·1) 10·626   0·26) 1·1102

1·7) 10·778   3·4) 13·090   2·2) 11·550   0·27) 1·1502   3·1) 19·437

F

11·2) 58·464   1·04) 4·9192   15·1) 91·355   1·16) 2·3896   21·3) 72·846

20·5) 22·140   0·141) 0·16074   13·2) 26·928   2·08) 3·2240   16·1) 34·776

G Divide

5·130 by 1·5	17·028 by 3·6
18·846 by 0·27	8·7464 by 1·16
5·6945 by 0·35	31·570 by 2·2
4·2140 by 0·35	47·7963 by 2·07
15·906 by 0·22	92·923 by 4·3
1·4464 by 0·32	1·4028 by 0·21

Approximations with decimals

A Write these quantities correct to the **a** third **b** second **c** first place of decimals.

2·1274	3·9681	4·0127	5·3482	6·7296
10·1206	9·0079	6·2396	16·2574	8·3521

B Work these answers correct to one place of decimals.

$7\overline{)4{\cdot}49}$ $5\overline{)15{\cdot}75}$ $4\overline{)5{\cdot}3}$ $6\overline{)25{\cdot}61}$ $8\overline{)1{\cdot}7}$

$0{\cdot}3\overline{)0{\cdot}389}$ $0{\cdot}9\overline{)6{\cdot}5}$ $0{\cdot}2\overline{)0{\cdot}165}$ $0{\cdot}11\overline{)0{\cdot}1677}$ $0{\cdot}12\overline{)0{\cdot}223}$

$1{\cdot}4\overline{)0{\cdot}465}$ $0{\cdot}26\overline{)0{\cdot}8934}$ $2{\cdot}3\overline{)3{\cdot}29}$ $0{\cdot}17\overline{)1{\cdot}399}$ $1{\cdot}3\overline{)6{\cdot}067}$

C Work these answers correct to two places of decimals.

$7\overline{)2{\cdot}99}$ $8\overline{)8{\cdot}846}$ $9\overline{)18{\cdot}941}$ $12\overline{)7{\cdot}51}$ $11\overline{)46{\cdot}377}$

$0{\cdot}2\overline{)0{\cdot}1821}$ $0{\cdot}4\overline{)0{\cdot}2905}$ $0{\cdot}6\overline{)1{\cdot}616}$ $0{\cdot}3\overline{)1{\cdot}418}$ $0{\cdot}5\overline{)1{\cdot}9267}$

$0{\cdot}27\overline{)0{\cdot}6062}$ $0{\cdot}26\overline{)0{\cdot}37154}$ $2{\cdot}1\overline{)4{\cdot}337}$ $2{\cdot}4\overline{)4{\cdot}3292}$

D Work these answers correct to three places of decimals.

$12\overline{)4{\cdot}0999}$ $8\overline{)3{\cdot}6207}$ $7\overline{)1{\cdot}905}$ $11\overline{)4{\cdot}379}$

$0{\cdot}7\overline{)3{\cdot}30518}$ $0{\cdot}6\overline{)1{\cdot}5617}$ $0{\cdot}3\overline{)10{\cdot}264}$ $0{\cdot}4\overline{)5{\cdot}2126}$

$1{\cdot}3\overline{)0{\cdot}81529}$ $2{\cdot}9\overline{)7{\cdot}3458}$ $0{\cdot}47\overline{)2{\cdot}02135}$ $1{\cdot}8\overline{)1{\cdot}96295}$

E Work each of these answers correct to **a** three places **b** two places **c** one place of decimals.

0·2148 ÷ 0·13	1·6277 ÷ 2·3	3·47115 ÷ 1·7
8·3291 ÷ 0·37	0·413156 ÷ 0·15	2·7119 ÷ 2·6

Money practice — addition and subtraction

A 1 Give the change you would receive from   **a** a fifty   **b** a pound   if you spent:

| 23p? | £0·47? | 38p? | £0·27? | 41p? | £0·12? |

| £0·16? | 48p? | 35p? | £0·33? | 9p? | £0·25? |

2 Give the total of each of these six amounts of money.

	£5	£1	50p	20p	10p	5p	2p	1p	total
a	2	1	5	6		8	7	3	
b	1	9	3	12	7	5	8	1	
c		12	7	5	4	6	5		
d	5			21	5	4	6	2	
e	3	4		7	9		12	6	
f	2	5	4	7	8	10	2	3	

B

£8·12 + 0·17 + £4·47   £145·26 + £73·88

£24·76 + £18·07 + £0·99   £134·14 + £26·99

£16·43 + £21·16 + £34·34   £232·67 + £141·75

£23·16 + £15·27 + £47·43   £134·16 + £362·15

£19·04 + £16·12 + £0·79   £204·19 + £96·82

C   £73·16 − £47·88   £200 − £147·16

£146·08 − £79·76   £152·20 − £123·18

£104·26 − £93·69   £140·36 − £73·49

£147·32 − £66·45   £194·07 − £189·22

£99·00 − £43·43   £250 − £236·86

Money practice — multiplication and division

A 1

no	item	cost each	total
7	tin of beans	21p	
3	tin of meat	67p	
6	loaf	42p	
5	bag of sugar	53p	
8	packet of tea	46p	
9	jelly	17p	
4	packet of cereals	72p	

Copy and complete the table.

2 What is

$\frac{1}{6}$ of   24p   96p   30p   36p   12p   54p   42p?

$\frac{1}{4}$ of   24p   52p   44p   36p   28p   32p   48p?

$\frac{1}{3}$ of   39p   33p   21p   36p   27p   51p   24p?

$\frac{1}{8}$ of   32p   40p   48p   56p   64p   80p   72p?

B

£6·17 × 7   £25·06 × 9   £0·87 × 12

£18.42 × 6   £23·27 × 11   £41·36 × 8

£0·17 × 15   £1·16 × 23   £2·19 × 21

£32·41 × 25   £6·24 × 18   £16·48 × 19

C

£74·40 ÷ 12   £134·47 ÷ 7   £45·81 ÷ 9

£46·53 ÷ 11   £90·20 ÷ 8   £100·86 ÷ 6

£54·99 ÷ 13   £42·49 ÷ 7   £20·25 ÷ 15

£30·38 ÷ 14   £94·76 ÷ 23   £3·74 ÷ 17

D Multiply $\frac{1}{5}$ of £2·70 by 6.

Divide 7 times £2·31 by 3.

Costing

1 Find the cost of:

500 g at 96p per kg	$2\frac{1}{2}$ kg at 76p per $\frac{1}{2}$ kg
400 ml at £1·20 per litre	50 cm at 62p per metre
6 m at 27p per metre	$5\frac{1}{2}$ l at 13p per $\frac{1}{4}$ litre
700 g at 30p per kg	700 mm at 70p per metre
250 ml at 48p per litre	6·5 kg at 13p per 0·5 kg

2 Copy and complete the table.

	1 kg	500 g	200 g	100 g
	£1·00			
	50p			
	40p			
	30p			
	20p			

Find the cost of

700 g at 50p per kg	300 g at 40p per kg
800 g at 30p per kg	300 g at 20p per kg
600 g at 20p per kg	600 g at 30p per kg

3 Find the cost of

500 g at 60p per kg   400 g 50p per kg   250 g at £1·20 per kg

100 g at 90p per kg   500 g at £1·40 per kg   700 g at 70p per kg

4 Pork costs 70p per $\frac{1}{2}$ kg. Find the cost of

100 g   200 g   50 g   500 g   450 g   350 g   950 g   550 g

5 $3\frac{1}{2}$ metres of cloth costs £1·47. Find the cost of

$\frac{1}{2}$ m   1 m $4\frac{1}{2}$ m $6\frac{1}{2}$ m   3 m $2\frac{1}{2}$ m   7 m   9 m

6 Envelopes cost 40p for 50. Find the cost of

100   25   200   400   350   750   225   275   375   425

7 $1\frac{1}{4}$ litres of orange squash costs 80p. How much for

$\frac{1}{4}$ l $\frac{1}{2}$ l $\frac{3}{4}$ l   1 l $2\frac{1}{2}$ l $3\frac{3}{4}$ l $4\frac{1}{4}$ l   5 l $5\frac{1}{2}$ l $6\frac{1}{4}$ l

Profit and loss

A 1 Copy and complete.

cost price	£3·25	£5·50	£8·20	£10·50	£15·60	£18·50
selling price	£4·00	£6·99	£9·35	£11·49	£17·39	£19·99
profit						

2 Copy and complete the table showing the sale of damaged goods.

cost price	£7·50	£9·50	£12·50	£15·25	£17·75	£20·50
selling price	£6·25	£7·45	£10·75	£13·80	£16·95	£14·65
loss						

B 1 A car was bought for £2,575. It was sold later for £1,950. What was the loss?

2 What must a £3·50 box of apples be sold at to make a profit of 85p?

3 A shopkeeper buys 400 lettuce at 11p each. How much profit will he make if he sells them at 14p each?

4 A dealer pays £24·50, £32·60, £29·80, and £16·50 for four tables. He sells the tables for £130·00 altogether. What is his average profit per table?

5 Fourteen pairs of ladders each cost £7·25. How much must each pair be sold for, to make a total profit of £35·00?

6 15 chairs were bought for £138·75. **a** How much each did they cost? **b** If each chair was sold for £12·50, what was the total profit?

7 Four shop-soiled carpets which cost £262 altogether, are sold at £49·95 each. What is the amount of money lost?

8 How much would be saved by buying a car for £6,750 cash instead of paying 24 payments of £325·75?

Fractional values

A Express in lowest terms **a** the shaded part **b** the unshaded part.

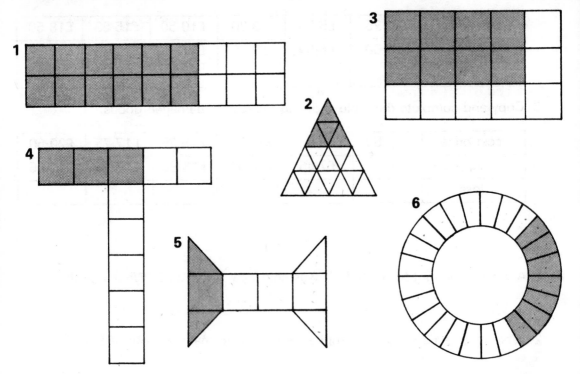

B How many

halves	$2\frac{1}{2}$	$3\frac{1}{2}$	$4\frac{1}{2}$	5	6	$9\frac{1}{2}$	7	8	?
tenths	$2\frac{1}{5}$	$3\frac{3}{10}$	$4\frac{3}{5}$	$2\frac{1}{10}$	$6\frac{7}{10}$	$3\frac{4}{5}$	$1\frac{9}{10}$	$2\frac{2}{5}$	?
sixteenths	$1\frac{1}{16}$	$2\frac{1}{8}$	$3\frac{11}{16}$	$1\frac{15}{16}$	$3\frac{5}{8}$	$3\frac{7}{8}$	$2\frac{9}{16}$	$4\frac{5}{16}$	?
fifths	$2\frac{1}{5}$	$6\frac{3}{5}$	$3\frac{1}{5}$	$2\frac{2}{5}$	$4\frac{3}{5}$	$6\frac{3}{5}$	$2\frac{4}{5}$	$5\frac{4}{5}$	?

C Complete the series with fractions in lowest terms.

$\frac{1}{2}$ $\frac{7}{12}$ ☐ $\frac{3}{4}$ ☐ $\frac{11}{12}$

$\frac{1}{4}$ $\frac{3}{10}$ $\frac{7}{20}$ ☐ $\frac{9}{20}$ ☐

$1\frac{1}{3}$ $1\frac{1}{2}$ ☐ $1\frac{5}{6}$ ☐

$2\frac{14}{15}$ $2\frac{13}{15}$ ☐ $2\frac{11}{15}$ ☐ ☐

$6\frac{19}{24}$ $6\frac{3}{4}$ $6\frac{17}{24}$ ☐ $3\frac{5}{8}$ ☐ ☐

$\frac{13}{16}$ $\frac{3}{4}$ $\frac{11}{16}$ ☐ $\frac{9}{16}$ $\frac{1}{2}$ ☐ ☐

D Arrange in order of size — smallest first.

$3\frac{4}{5}$ $3\frac{13}{20}$ $3\frac{7}{10}$ $3\frac{3}{4}$

$1\frac{3}{4}$ $1\frac{5}{8}$ $1\frac{9}{16}$ $1\frac{15}{32}$

$3\frac{2}{3}$ $3\frac{5}{6}$ $3\frac{4}{9}$ $3\frac{7}{12}$

$6\frac{7}{24}$ $6\frac{1}{3}$ $6\frac{3}{8}$ $6\frac{1}{4}$

$4\frac{7}{15}$ $4\frac{3}{10}$ $4\frac{2}{5}$ $4\frac{9}{20}$

$2\frac{23}{24}$ $2\frac{11}{18}$ $2\frac{7}{12}$ $2\frac{5}{6}$

Fractions — addition

A 1 Give the lowest common multiple for

4 and 8	3 and 6	5 and 10	10 and 20	8 and 16
2 and 5	4 and 5	3 and 8	2 and 9	3 and 7
5 and 6	4 and 6	4 and 3	7 and 5	6 and 8

2 Change to mixed numbers.

$$\frac{15}{4} \qquad \frac{27}{10} \qquad \frac{36}{7} \qquad \frac{41}{8} \qquad \frac{15}{6} \qquad \frac{29}{20} \qquad \frac{20}{3} \qquad \frac{23}{11}$$

B

$$\frac{3}{5}+\frac{5}{8} \qquad \frac{2}{3}+\frac{7}{12} \qquad \frac{9}{24}+\frac{7}{10} \qquad \frac{7}{8}+\frac{3}{10}$$

$$\frac{8}{9}+\frac{1}{6} \qquad \frac{13}{25}+\frac{9}{10} \qquad \frac{3}{4}+\frac{4}{5} \qquad \frac{13}{16}+\frac{5}{8}$$

$$\frac{13}{20}+\frac{3}{5} \qquad \frac{3}{4}+\frac{7}{8} \qquad \frac{11}{12}+\frac{5}{8} \qquad \frac{9}{11}+\frac{1}{2}$$

C

$$4\tfrac{3}{5}+2\tfrac{1}{10} \qquad 2\tfrac{7}{8}+3\tfrac{5}{16} \qquad 6\tfrac{7}{20}+4\tfrac{7}{10} \qquad 1\tfrac{5}{8}+\tfrac{11}{16}$$

$$\tfrac{19}{20}+1\tfrac{3}{4} \qquad 3\tfrac{5}{6}+4\tfrac{11}{12} \qquad 2\tfrac{19}{25}+4\tfrac{4}{5} \qquad 5\tfrac{5}{18}+2\tfrac{2}{3}$$

$$\tfrac{19}{24}+6\tfrac{1}{6} \qquad 9\tfrac{2}{3}+4\tfrac{7}{15} \qquad 2\tfrac{4}{5}+8\tfrac{3}{4} \qquad 5\tfrac{9}{22}+2\tfrac{1}{2}$$

D

$$\tfrac{7}{13}+\tfrac{19}{26} \qquad \tfrac{4}{5}+\tfrac{11}{12} \qquad \tfrac{7}{15}+\tfrac{5}{12} \qquad \tfrac{5}{9}+\tfrac{4}{5}$$

$$\tfrac{5}{6}+\tfrac{8}{9} \qquad \tfrac{19}{20}+\tfrac{11}{30} \qquad \tfrac{7}{8}+\tfrac{8}{9} \qquad \tfrac{7}{15}+\tfrac{29}{30}$$

$$\tfrac{11}{15}+\tfrac{41}{45} \qquad \tfrac{23}{24}+\tfrac{19}{36} \qquad \tfrac{5}{7}+\tfrac{1}{6} \qquad \tfrac{6}{7}+\tfrac{5}{9}$$

E

$$3\tfrac{5}{18}+2\tfrac{7}{12} \qquad 6\tfrac{5}{7}+3\tfrac{5}{14} \qquad 9\tfrac{7}{16}+6\tfrac{3}{10} \qquad 2\tfrac{6}{7}+5\tfrac{2}{9}$$

$$7\tfrac{1}{13}+5\tfrac{4}{39} \qquad 6\tfrac{7}{20}+8\tfrac{8}{15} \qquad 2\tfrac{4}{9}+3\tfrac{4}{15} \qquad 8\tfrac{5}{33}+4\tfrac{7}{11}$$

$$4\tfrac{1}{15}+8\tfrac{19}{60} \qquad 2\tfrac{2}{3}+1\tfrac{19}{20} \qquad 6\tfrac{4}{7}+5\tfrac{3}{4} \qquad 4\tfrac{5}{12}+3\tfrac{9}{15}$$

F

$$7\tfrac{7}{8}+5\tfrac{13}{20}+6\tfrac{4}{5} \qquad\qquad 8\tfrac{11}{15}+4\tfrac{13}{20}+6\tfrac{19}{30}$$

Fractions — subtraction

A 1 Give the lowest common denominator for

$\frac{1}{20}$ and $\frac{1}{30}$ $\qquad$ $\frac{1}{25}$ and $\frac{1}{10}$ $\qquad$ $\frac{1}{16}$ and $\frac{1}{24}$ $\qquad$ $\frac{1}{12}$ and $\frac{1}{10}$

$\frac{1}{15}$ and $\frac{1}{12}$ $\qquad$ $\frac{1}{25}$ and $\frac{1}{4}$ $\qquad$ $\frac{1}{14}$ and $\frac{1}{21}$ $\qquad$ $\frac{1}{9}$ and $\frac{1}{8}$

$\frac{1}{20}$ and $\frac{1}{6}$ $\qquad$ $\frac{1}{8}$ and $\frac{1}{5}$ $\qquad$ $\frac{1}{13}$ and $\frac{1}{4}$ $\qquad$ $\frac{1}{7}$ and $\frac{1}{9}$

2 What are the missing numerators?

$\dfrac{7}{20} = \dfrac{\square}{40}$ $\qquad$ $\dfrac{7}{8} = \dfrac{\square}{56}$ $\qquad$ $\dfrac{2}{9} = \dfrac{\square}{63}$ $\qquad$ $\dfrac{11}{25} = \dfrac{\square}{50}$

$\dfrac{\square}{20} = \dfrac{4}{5}$ $\qquad$ $\dfrac{\square}{28} = \dfrac{5}{7}$ $\qquad$ $\dfrac{\square}{60} = \dfrac{9}{15}$ $\qquad$ $\dfrac{\square}{15} = \dfrac{2}{3}$

B $\quad \frac{7}{8} - \frac{3}{4}$ $\qquad$ $\frac{9}{10} - \frac{11}{20}$ $\qquad$ $\frac{5}{6} - \frac{17}{24}$ $\qquad$ $\frac{15}{16} - \frac{3}{4}$

$\frac{9}{11} - \frac{1}{2}$ $\qquad$ $\frac{24}{25} - \frac{4}{5}$ $\qquad$ $\frac{3}{4} - \frac{1}{6}$ $\qquad$ $\frac{7}{12} - \frac{1}{5}$

$\frac{17}{40} - \frac{19}{80}$ $\qquad$ $\frac{6}{7} - \frac{9}{21}$ $\qquad$ $\frac{8}{9} - \frac{15}{18}$ $\qquad$ $\frac{13}{16} - \frac{3}{8}$

C $\quad 2\frac{1}{3} - 1\frac{5}{8}$ $\qquad$ $4\frac{3}{4} - 2\frac{9}{10}$ $\qquad$ $6\frac{7}{8} - 3\frac{3}{10}$ $\qquad$ $7\frac{4}{7} - 2\frac{3}{14}$

$8\frac{7}{10} - 4\frac{3}{4}$ $\qquad$ $2\frac{4}{5} - 1\frac{7}{20}$ $\qquad$ $9\frac{19}{24} - 6\frac{1}{3}$ $\qquad$ $5\frac{5}{8} - 3\frac{1}{12}$

$9\frac{4}{25} - 3\frac{11}{50}$ $\qquad$ $4\frac{3}{4} - 3\frac{2}{3}$ $\qquad$ $5\frac{5}{12} - 3\frac{5}{6}$ $\qquad$ $2\frac{9}{10} - 1\frac{1}{2}$

D $\quad \frac{19}{30} - \frac{7}{20}$ $\qquad$ $\frac{6}{7} - \frac{5}{9}$ $\qquad$ $\frac{7}{9} - \frac{8}{15}$ $\qquad$ $\frac{4}{5} - \frac{11}{45}$

$\frac{19}{25} - \frac{35}{50}$ $\qquad$ $\frac{19}{20} - \frac{5}{6}$ $\qquad$ $\frac{17}{18} - \frac{7}{12}$ $\qquad$ $\frac{7}{8} - \frac{6}{7}$

$\frac{6}{13} - \frac{1}{4}$ $\qquad$ $\frac{11}{15} - \frac{5}{12}$ $\qquad$ $\frac{7}{11} - \frac{14}{33}$ $\qquad$ $\frac{9}{14} - \frac{5}{21}$

E $\quad 2\frac{7}{9} - 1\frac{9}{10}$ $\qquad$ $9\frac{5}{16} - 6\frac{17}{24}$ $\qquad$ $10\frac{7}{30} - 5\frac{1}{4}$ $\qquad$ $5\frac{11}{15} - 3\frac{23}{25}$

$3\frac{1}{3} - 2\frac{7}{20}$ $\qquad$ $2\frac{11}{12} - 1\frac{7}{10}$ $\qquad$ $7\frac{2}{9} - 4\frac{2}{27}$ $\qquad$ $5\frac{2}{3} - 3\frac{9}{16}$

$5\frac{7}{8} - 1\frac{4}{5}$ $\qquad$ $8\frac{3}{10} - 6\frac{19}{25}$ $\qquad$ $2\frac{11}{16} - 1\frac{5}{12}$ $\qquad$ $4\frac{9}{20} - 2\frac{11}{15}$

F $\quad 6\frac{3}{8} + 5\frac{4}{5} - 7\frac{9}{20}$ $\qquad\qquad\qquad$ $8\frac{13}{20} + 4\frac{3}{5} - 6\frac{2}{3}$

$5\frac{3}{4} - 2\frac{7}{12} + 6\frac{3}{10}$ $\qquad\qquad\qquad$ $11\frac{11}{12} - 8\frac{7}{16} + 5\frac{5}{24}$

Fractions — multiplication

A 1 Cancel to lowest terms.

$\frac{45}{50}$ $\frac{36}{48}$ $\frac{33}{45}$ $\frac{60}{72}$ $\frac{25}{100}$ $\frac{45}{60}$ $\frac{18}{27}$ $\frac{36}{42}$ $\frac{72}{80}$ $\frac{52}{65}$

2 Change to improper fractions.

$7\frac{3}{4}$ $8\frac{5}{6}$ $9\frac{2}{13}$ $1\frac{7}{12}$ $4\frac{13}{20}$ $2\frac{7}{10}$ $5\frac{11}{16}$ $4\frac{1}{60}$ $2\frac{2}{15}$ $1\frac{7}{30}$

B $\frac{4}{5} \times \frac{15}{20}$　　$\frac{3}{8} \times \frac{24}{25}$　　$\frac{19}{20} \times \frac{6}{7}$　　$\frac{3}{4} \times \frac{8}{9}$

$\frac{11}{12} \times \frac{6}{11}$　　$\frac{15}{16} \times \frac{4}{5}$　　$\frac{13}{20} \times \frac{8}{9}$　　$\frac{21}{25} \times \frac{15}{16}$

$\frac{2}{3} \times \frac{9}{10}$　　$\frac{14}{15} \times \frac{17}{21}$　　$\frac{11}{40} \times \frac{10}{11}$　　$\frac{9}{16} \times \frac{4}{15}$

C $2\frac{1}{5} \times 2\frac{3}{4}$　　$4\frac{1}{4} \times 1\frac{1}{3}$　　$2\frac{4}{5} \times 1\frac{3}{7}$　　$2\frac{1}{10} \times 2\frac{1}{6}$

$5\frac{1}{2} \times 2\frac{2}{5}$　　$7\frac{1}{2} \times 1\frac{3}{10}$　　$6\frac{1}{4} \times 2\frac{2}{15}$　　$3\frac{1}{3} \times 1\frac{1}{20}$

$2\frac{4}{5} \times 5\frac{1}{4}$　　$6\frac{2}{3} \times \frac{9}{10}$　　$2\frac{7}{10} \times 6\frac{2}{3}$　　$4\frac{4}{5} \times 2\frac{1}{12}$

D $\frac{15}{16} \times \frac{24}{25}$　　$\frac{11}{60} \times \frac{48}{55}$　　$\frac{13}{14} \times \frac{28}{39}$　　$\frac{15}{28} \times \frac{7}{10}$

$\frac{8}{45} \times \frac{15}{32}$　　$\frac{18}{25} \times \frac{15}{28}$　　$\frac{22}{25} \times \frac{30}{33}$　　$\frac{11}{24} \times \frac{2}{7}$

$\frac{9}{56} \times \frac{21}{25}$　　$\frac{3}{49} \times \frac{14}{45}$　　$\frac{13}{18} \times \frac{27}{52}$　　$\frac{35}{36} \times \frac{48}{55}$

E $\frac{5}{12} \times 1\frac{7}{15}$　　$6\frac{2}{3} \times 1\frac{8}{25}$　　$4\frac{2}{7} \times 2\frac{1}{10}$　　$2\frac{13}{18} \times 5\frac{1}{7}$

$2\frac{7}{24} \times 2\frac{2}{11}$　　$1\frac{5}{16} \times 2\frac{2}{21}$　　$3\frac{1}{9} \times 2\frac{1}{4}$　　$1\frac{19}{36} \times 9\frac{3}{5}$

F $\frac{7}{8} \times \frac{4}{5} \times \frac{5}{21}$　　　　$\frac{13}{16} \times \frac{12}{25} \times \frac{15}{26}$

$\frac{2}{3} \times \frac{9}{10} \times \frac{25}{27}$　　　　$\frac{11}{60} \times \frac{24}{33} \times \frac{9}{14}$

G $2\frac{1}{2} \times 3\frac{1}{5} \times 3\frac{3}{4}$　　　　$2\frac{2}{9} \times 1\frac{5}{6} \times 1\frac{3}{22}$

$1\frac{5}{16} \times 1\frac{1}{9} \times 4\frac{4}{5}$　　　　$5\frac{1}{7} \times 4\frac{2}{3} \times 2\frac{3}{8}$

Fractions—division

A Give the highest common factor of

45 and 60	63 and 21	24 and 36	25 and 35
21 and 28	80 and 100	24 and 32	15 and 18
25 and 75	60 and 48	44 and 66	72 and 84

B Change to improper fractions.

$2\frac{7}{8}$ $\quad$ $5\frac{13}{14}$ $\quad$ $4\frac{5}{6}$ $\quad$ $3\frac{11}{12}$ $\quad$ $8\frac{13}{20}$ $\quad$ $2\frac{19}{25}$ $\quad$ $5\frac{3}{16}$ $\quad$ $8\frac{7}{10}$

C $\frac{4}{5} \div \frac{8}{15}$ $\qquad$ $\frac{3}{10} \div \frac{9}{25}$ $\qquad$ $\frac{5}{16} \div \frac{15}{16}$ $\qquad$ $\frac{7}{8} \div \frac{14}{15}$

$\frac{11}{12} \div \frac{7}{24}$ $\qquad$ $\frac{13}{21} \div \frac{5}{7}$ $\qquad$ $\frac{9}{20} \div \frac{6}{25}$ $\qquad$ $\frac{8}{35} \div \frac{16}{21}$

$\frac{7}{24} \div \frac{5}{16}$ $\qquad$ $\frac{11}{50} \div \frac{22}{25}$ $\qquad$ $\frac{35}{36} \div \frac{25}{48}$ $\qquad$ $\frac{17}{20} \div \frac{23}{60}$

D $2\frac{1}{2} \div 2\frac{2}{5}$ $\qquad$ $7\frac{3}{5} \div 10\frac{2}{5}$ $\qquad$ $6\frac{1}{4} \div 1\frac{3}{7}$ $\qquad$ $8\frac{1}{3} \div 1\frac{7}{8}$

$12\frac{1}{2} \div 8\frac{3}{4}$ $\qquad$ $2\frac{1}{7} \div 2\frac{13}{16}$ $\qquad$ $2\frac{7}{10} \div 2\frac{1}{10}$ $\qquad$ $1\frac{6}{7} \div 9\frac{3}{4}$

$1\frac{13}{20} \div 4\frac{8}{9}$ $\qquad$ $2\frac{2}{5} \div 1\frac{5}{11}$ $\qquad$ $5\frac{5}{8} \div 3\frac{3}{4}$ $\qquad$ $3\frac{8}{9} \div 2\frac{6}{7}$

E $\frac{14}{25} \div \frac{28}{45}$ $\qquad$ $\frac{33}{45} \div \frac{66}{75}$ $\qquad$ $\frac{15}{16} \div \frac{73}{80}$ $\qquad$ $\frac{18}{19} \div \frac{27}{38}$

$\frac{20}{21} \div \frac{10}{63}$ $\qquad$ $\frac{45}{77} \div \frac{20}{33}$ $\qquad$ $\frac{75}{77} \div \frac{25}{44}$ $\qquad$ $\frac{26}{45} \div \frac{13}{30}$

F $2\frac{22}{25} \div 2\frac{7}{10}$ $\qquad$ $3\frac{7}{15} \div 2\frac{3}{5}$ $\qquad$ $\frac{19}{36} \div 4\frac{3}{4}$ $\qquad$ $7\frac{3}{7} \div 2\frac{8}{9}$

$4\frac{2}{7} \div 3\frac{7}{11}$ $\qquad$ $2\frac{2}{15} \div \frac{16}{25}$ $\qquad$ $8\frac{1}{10} \div 1\frac{19}{35}$ $\qquad$ $4\frac{8}{11} \div 5\frac{1}{5}$

G $3\frac{3}{4} \times \frac{12}{15} \div 1\frac{4}{5}$ $\qquad\qquad$ $4\frac{3}{8} \times 1\frac{4}{5} \div 1\frac{5}{16}$

$2\frac{4}{19} \times 4\frac{2}{9} \div 2\frac{5}{8}$ $\qquad\qquad$ $4\frac{1}{11} \times 3\frac{3}{10} \div 2\frac{1}{4}$

H $(1\frac{4}{5} - \frac{7}{10}) \div (5\frac{3}{4} + 2\frac{1}{2})$ $\qquad$ $(2\frac{5}{16} - \frac{5}{8}) \div (4\frac{5}{6} - 2\frac{7}{12})$

$(3\frac{1}{3} + 4\frac{5}{6}) \div (3\frac{2}{5} - 1\frac{3}{10})$ $\qquad$ $(6\frac{2}{5} - 4\frac{3}{8}) \div (2\frac{1}{2} + 1\frac{11}{20})$

Fractions — mixed examples

A 1 Change to vulgar fractions in lowest terms.

0·53   1·17   2·35   4·8   14·325   6·03

11·006   15·75   12·62   19·47   0·015   3·426

2 Change to decimal fractions.

$2\frac{3}{10}$ $4\frac{7}{20}$ $6\frac{9}{25}$ $11\frac{7}{10}$ $13\frac{4}{5}$ $6\frac{17}{50}$ $\frac{19}{1000}$ $1\frac{17}{20}$

$5\frac{3}{8}$ $9\frac{14}{25}$ $7\frac{13}{20}$ $6\frac{5}{8}$ $\frac{37}{1000}$ $2\frac{17}{500}$ $1\frac{31}{250}$ $7\frac{113}{125}$

$2\frac{7}{8}$ $3\frac{13}{1000}$ $4\frac{73}{250}$ $6\frac{97}{125}$ $6\frac{151}{500}$ $1\frac{18}{25}$ $\frac{11}{20}$ $2\frac{479}{500}$

B Change to decimal fractions by dividing.

Example: $\frac{1}{5} = 5\overline{)1·0}$ with $0·2$ above.

1 $\frac{9}{10}$ $\frac{19}{20}$ $\frac{3}{5}$ $\frac{16}{25}$ $\frac{1}{8}$ $\frac{3}{20}$ $\frac{11}{125}$ $\frac{39}{50}$ $\frac{67}{500}$ $\frac{3}{8}$ $\frac{9}{20}$ $\frac{21}{25}$

2 $4\frac{7}{8}$ $2\frac{3}{10}$ $6\frac{2}{5}$ $8\frac{7}{25}$ $5\frac{1}{20}$ $2\frac{51}{125}$ $4\frac{37}{50}$ $6\frac{431}{500}$

C Change to decimal fractions by dividing. Give your answer correct to 3 places of decimal.

1 $\frac{7}{11}$ $\frac{14}{15}$ $\frac{7}{9}$ $\frac{13}{16}$ $\frac{2}{7}$ $\frac{11}{12}$ $\frac{5}{6}$ $\frac{5}{21}$ $\frac{17}{18}$ $\frac{2}{3}$

2 $4\frac{5}{13}$ $2\frac{13}{18}$ $5\frac{3}{14}$ $9\frac{19}{33}$ $6\frac{10}{11}$ $8\frac{13}{15}$ $2\frac{11}{16}$ $1\frac{9}{17}$

D Arrange in order of size — largest first.

1 $\frac{5}{12}$ 0·53 $\frac{5}{8}$ $\frac{5}{11}$ 0·473 $\frac{4}{9}$ 0·432

2 0·251 $\frac{3}{8}$ $\frac{3}{10}$ 0·335 $\frac{4}{15}$ $\frac{5}{18}$ 0·326

3 0·755 $\frac{15}{24}$ $\frac{19}{25}$ 0·695 $\frac{8}{11}$ 0·732 $\frac{13}{16}$

Fractions — problems

A Calculate

$\frac{7}{10}$ of   **a** £4·35   **b** 12 m   **c** 550   **d** 7·9   **e** 2·75 km

$\frac{5}{8}$ of   **a** 320   **b** 3·48 l   **c** 2 040   **d** 640 g   **e** 780 mm

$\frac{11}{20}$ of   **a** 22 040   **b** £17·60   **c** $2\frac{3}{4}$ kg   **d** 960 m   **e** 23 tonnes

B Find the whole when

a $\frac{3}{4}$ is 342   **b** $\frac{5}{8}$ is 265 g   **c** $\frac{9}{10}$ is 891 l   **d** $\frac{5}{6}$ is $12\frac{1}{2}$

e $\frac{11}{12}$ is 352 p   **f** $\frac{14}{15}$ is 294 m   **g** $\frac{19}{20}$ is 57 km   **h** $\frac{7}{11}$ is $5\frac{1}{4}$

C **1** Anne walks $\frac{4}{5}$ km to school. John walks $\frac{3}{4}$ km to school. How much further does Anne walk?

2 A third of Peter's money is 75p. What would $\frac{3}{5}$ be?

3 In a collection of stamps, $\frac{7}{20}$ were British, $\frac{1}{10}$ were Commonwealth. The total number of stamps in the collection was 460. How many stamps were **a** British   **b** Commonwealth   **c** other countries   ?

4 Anne spends $\frac{2}{3}$ of her money on a dress, $\frac{1}{4}$ on a pair of shoes and has £2·50 left. How much money did **a** she have to begin with   **b** the dress cost   **c** the shoes cost   ?

5 In four days a car travels $12\frac{3}{4}$ km, $16\frac{2}{3}$ km, $19\frac{7}{10}$ km and $8\frac{1}{2}$ km. How far did it travel altogether?

6 Take the sum of $4\frac{3}{10}$ and $2\frac{11}{12}$ from the difference between $4\frac{4}{5}$ and $12\frac{7}{10}$.

〜 product of   **a** $4\frac{2}{7}$ and $4\frac{9}{10}$ **b** $8\frac{1}{10}$ and $2\frac{7}{9}$.

⸆t the sum of $4\frac{3}{16}$ and $2\frac{5}{8}$ from the product of $5\frac{1}{7}$ and $1\frac{5}{12}$.

Decimal and number-problems

1 An athlete throws a javelin 52·74 m, 55·36 m, 51·99 m, 55·63 m. What was his average throw?

2

	Jones	Smith	Brown	Gray	Young	Old
1st dive	52·31	51·62	52·53	50·29	54·25	49·29
2nd dive	50·43	53·11	50·23	54·35	51·06	54·92
3rd dive	49·66	49·28	54·55	51·64	50·65	53·55
4th dive	54·04	52·39	48·65	52·32	49·36	48·36

The table shows the marks scored by 6 divers in a diving competition. Who was leading after   a the 1st dive   b the 2nd dive   c the 3rd dive   d 4th dive   ? Which diver had the highest average dive?

3 A farmer plants 125 rows of cabbage with 147 in each row. How many cabbages altogether?

4 There are six turnstiles for the paddock of a football ground. 2475 people went through the 1st turnstile, 1472 the second, 1062 the third, 2025 the fourth, 1001 the fifth, and 2216 the sixth.
a How many people were in the paddock?
b If the cost was 95p, how much money was taken?

5 A lorry can carry 2475 boxes of eggs. How many boxes are carried by   a 48 lorries   b 65 lorries   c 55 lorries   ? If one egg box holds 144 eggs, how many eggs can one lorry carry?

6 A turnstile at a museum shows 36 431 when the museum opens and 38 279 when it closes. How many people have visited the museum?

7 A pools win of £15,750·63 is won by 23 workers. What is each worker's share?

8 Find the product of   a 2749 and 79   b 6758·73 and 85

9 Find the quotient of   a 56·032 and 1·7   b 336·4376 and 1·93

10 Divide the sum of 274·21 and 4326·83 by the difference between 124·02 and 123·78.

Percentages

A Use the signs $>$, $<$ or $=$ to complete the following.

8% $\frac{2}{25}$ 70% $\frac{4}{5}$ 35% $\frac{3}{10}$ 55% $\frac{11}{20}$

$\frac{3}{4}$ 65% $\frac{19}{20}$ 76% $\frac{17}{25}$ 72% $\frac{3}{5}$ 62%

$\frac{5}{8}$ $72\frac{1}{2}\%$ $\frac{3}{20}$ 12% $\frac{14}{25}$ 56% 32% $\frac{7}{20}$

B Find the value of

50% of 90	20% of £2·05	5% of 250 kg
10% of 120	50% of 36	10% of 970
4% of 325	$12\frac{1}{2}\%$ of 176	5% of 150
25% of 1000	10% of 325 l	2% of 600 g
20% of £3·50	5% of 80p	$12\frac{1}{2}\%$ of 64
25% of 480	2% of 2500	20% of 105

C Find the value of

1 a 4%   **b** 12%   **c** 16%   **d** 32%   **e** 48%   of 125

2 a 20%   **b** 40%   **c** 60%   **d** 80%   of £2·50

3 a 10%   **b** 30%   **c** 70%   **d** 90%   of 450

4 a 2%   **b** 6%   **c** 18%   **d** 34%   **e** 46%   of 300 g

5 a 5%   **b** 15%   **c** 35%   **d** 45%   **e** 55%   of £5·00

6 a $12\frac{1}{2}\%$ **b** $37\frac{1}{2}\%$ **c** $62\frac{1}{2}\%$ **d** $87\frac{1}{2}\%$ of 1000

D

10% of 50p =	70% of £3·50 =	45% of 330 m =
40% of 75 g =	25% of 84 kg =	26% of 150 t =
75% of 450 =	50% of £100 =	90% of 450p =
30% of 960p =	$12\frac{1}{2}\%$ of 72 =	35% of 80 =
12% of 175 cm =	16% of 50 =	80% of £625 =
60% of £5·00 =	20% of 550 l =	15% of 120 =

Percentages

1 Increase these numbers by **a** 10% **b** 25%.

| 490 | 750 | 680 | 484 | 768 | 924 |

2 Decrease each number by **a** 20% **b** 5%.

| 3754 | 8902 | 7426 | 6891 | 5249 | 7348 |

3

items	sale price	a	b
socks	95p		
shirts	£2·95		
shoes	£5·60		
ties	£1·25		
coats	£8·50		

The prices listed in the table are reduced by a further 10% for cash. Find **a** the extra reduction on each item **b** the reduced price for each item.

4 The cash price of a TV set is £320·00. If paid for over 12 months there is a deposit of £50 and a hire-purchase charge of 8%.
a How much HP is paid?
b What is the total cost buying on HP?
c How much would each monthly payment be?

5 How much discount would you receive if goods priced £57 had a 40% discount?

6 Footballs were marked 15% off. If a boy paid £4·25 for a football, what was the usual price?

7 Bank interest is 6%. How much interest would you receive on
a £174·50   **b** £2,456·50   **c** £24,496·00

8 76% of a group of 50 children passed a cycling test. How many children failed?

9 What should be paid for a £2,475 car on sale at $33\frac{1}{3}$% discount?

10 3471 is 75% of which number?

Ratio

A 1 Express as ratios.

a $\frac{11}{20}$ $\frac{9}{10}$ $\frac{4}{5}$ $\frac{12}{15}$ $\frac{21}{30}$ $\frac{7}{8}$ $\frac{11}{12}$ $\frac{19}{25}$ $\frac{33}{100}$ $\frac{29}{50}$

b   40%   35%   27% $12\frac{1}{2}\%$ 75%   30%   16%   14%

2 a   Change to vulgar fractions.

     3:4   6:7   27:40   33:50   23:100   7:8

   b   Change to percentages.

     7:20   9:50   13:25   18:25   3:10   23:100

B 1   **a** _____

     b _____

     c _____

     d _____

Give these ratios.

a:b   a:c   a:d   b:c   b:d   c:d

d:a   d:c   d:b   b:a   c:a   c:b

2 Measure and draw these lines. Divide each up to the given ratio.

     a _____

     b _____   **a**   4:3

                                         b   5:6

     c _____   **c**   1:3

                                         d   4:1

     d _____

C 1 Give the gradients for each of the following.

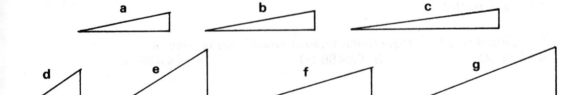

2 Draw slopes to show these gradients.

1:7   1:9   1:4   1:3   1:10

2:5   3:4   3:5   3:10   7:10

Check your drawings with the teacher.

Ratio and proportion

A Work out the rise if the gradient is

1 : 5   distance travelled 400 m   1 : 20   distance travelled 850 km

1 : 9   distance travelled 720 m   1 : 10   distance travelled 215 m

2 : 3   distance travelled 300 km   2 : 25   distance travelled 925 m

3 : 8   distance travelled 1 km   4 : 15   distance travelled 105 km

B 1 Divide each quantity into two parts in the ratio given.

  a 600 g ratio 1 : 5   **b** 45 children ratio 4 : 5
  c 24 sweets ratio 1 : 3   **d** 750 kg ratio 2 : 3
  e 110 trees ratio 10 : 1   **f** 60 oranges ratio 5 : 7

2 Each quantity has been broken into two parts. Give the ratio.

72	48 and 24	91 m	39 m and 52 m
144p	84p and 60p	£2·75	£1·50 and £1·25
150 g	50 g and 100 g	2200	800 and 1400
400 l	250 l and 150 l	240 cm	150 cm and 90 cm

C 1 A car rises 20 metres on a road with a gradient of 1 : 7. How far has it travelled?

2 On a length of railway track of 3 km the gradient is 1 : 30. How many metres does the track rise?

3 A tractor rises $2\frac{1}{2}$ m travelling up a 10 m ramp. What is the gradient?

D 1 £25 is shared between John and Alan so that Alan has four times as much as John. How much do they each have?

2 If 14 days holiday costs £35·00, how much would it cost for
  a 10 days?   **b** 15 days?   **c** 24 days?

Equations

A $84 \div (4 \times 3)$ =

$(24 \div 6) + (5 \times 6)$ =

$(9 \times 7) - 8$ =

$(7 \times 5) + (4 \times 3)$ =

$(121 \div 11) - (2 \times 4)$ =

$(7 \times 12) + 5$ =

$(63 \div 7) - 4$ =

$(15 \times 5) - (96 \div 12)$ =

$(27 \div 3) + (7 \times 11)$ =

$(99 \div 11) - (45 \div 9)$ =

B $76 + 35 = 82 + \boxed{}$

$129 - 50 = 85 - \boxed{}$

$\boxed{} + 16 = 35 + 12$

$150 - \boxed{} = 75 + 11$

$66 - \boxed{} = 29 + 12$

$131 + 65 = 96 + \boxed{}$

$150 - 73 = 49 + \boxed{}$

$\boxed{} + 72 = 96 - 12$

$67 - \boxed{} = 29 + 14$

$43 + \boxed{} = 56 - 6$

C $\frac{35}{5} + 9 =$

$38 - 17 \times 2 =$

$\frac{12}{3} + \frac{36}{6} - 7 =$

$2 \times 7 + 16 =$

$3 \times 9 + \frac{16}{4} =$

$125 - \frac{72}{6} =$

$25 \div 5 + 3 =$

$\frac{12}{2} + 7 + \frac{15}{3} =$

$6 \times 9 + 4 \times 5 =$

$\frac{15}{5} + \frac{72}{9} - \frac{12}{4} =$

D $\frac{27}{\boxed{}} + 7 = \frac{20}{4} + 11$

$\frac{\boxed{}}{8} + 3 \times 3 = 2 \times 3 + \frac{35}{5}$

$6 \times 8 - 4 = \boxed{} + \frac{48}{2}$

$12 \times 12 - 63 = 9 \times 9 + \boxed{}$

$10 \times 10 - \frac{36}{9} = \boxed{} - \frac{45}{9}$

$6 \times \boxed{} + 2 \times 6 = 20 + \frac{40}{4}$

$72 - \frac{45}{5} = 7 \times 8 + \boxed{}$

$6 \times 7 + 4 \times 9 = 4 \times 7 + \boxed{}$

$\frac{\boxed{}}{5} + 3 \times 4 = 7 \times 4 + 8$

$7 \times \boxed{} + 5 = 25 + 2 \times 11$

Expressions and equations

A $x = 3$ $y = 7$ $z = 9$ Give the value of

xy xyz $2x + 3$ $4z$ $2xy + 3xz$

$x + 5z$ $xy + yz$ $5y + 2z$ $x + y + 2z$ $6y + 3x$

B Find the value of x.

$3x + 1 = 10$ $5x + 3 = 28$ $2x - 2 = 6$ $x + 9 = 15$

$7x + 4 = 74$ $2x + 12 = 36$ $3x - 5 = 10$ $12x + 10 = 70$

C Write the expression for each statement.

6 less than x 4 times x 9 more than y $\frac{1}{2}$ of m

r decreased by 6 $\frac{1}{10}$ of 3 times h x more than 5

twice n plus r $\frac{1}{4} p$ minus t 15 less than v

D 1 Write the equation for each statement.

15 minus 3 times r equals 3 x divided by 3 is 12 $\frac{1}{8}$ of k is equal to 9

7 plus x equals twice 5   15 less than twice x equals 3   4 times x is 24

2 Solve the equations you have just written.

E Solve

$(6 \times 125) = (6 \times a) + (6 \times 120)$ $(4 \times 5) + (6 \times 5) = 10 \times x$

$(2 + 5) \times 4 = (2 \times y) + (5 \times y)$ $7 \times 96 = (q \times 96) + (q \times 0)$

$(2 \times 9) = (2 \times 3) + (2 \times n)$ $(36 \times 12) + (n \times 12) = 60 \times 12$

$(m \times 4) + (4 \times 4) = 48$ $30 \times 65 = (v \times 30) + (v \times 35)$

$7 \times (5 + 4) = x + 28$ $m \times 15 = (20 \times 15) + (10 \times 15)$

$5 \times (n + 7) = 25 + 35$ $6 \times 132 = (6 \times b) + (6 \times 100) + (6 \times 30)$

Roman numerals

A Write in our numerals.

1	XXV	IX	XXIII	XXVII	XIX	XXIV
2	XL	LXXXI	LXXVII	XLIV	LXXXIV	XLIII
3	CCC	CXCIV	CCLXXIX	CXLIX	CIV	CXCII
	CXC	CCXVII	CCXC	CXXV	CIX	CCXXX
4	DCCCL	CDIX	DXXXIX	CDLXXXVII	DCLIII	
	DXC	DCLXI	DLII	CDXXIV	CDLIV	
5	MDCC	MDCCCLIV	MCCCXXI	MCXLIV		
	MDCCXLV	MDCII	MCMLVII	MDCCCLII		

B Write in Roman numerals.

1	39	24	16	7	21	34	19	8
2	47	73	85	64	58	51	69	42
3	341	96	321	252	176	154	329	91
4	479	826	550	720	635	450	890	790
5	1947	1855	1432	1121	1840			
	1310	1705	1260	1502	1385			
	1688	1468	1940	1892				
6	43	96	1141	902	58	520	694	
7	354	1072	17	32	1220	87	143	
8	2250	1602	25	1111	2222	707	431	

Base 10

A Write in full in **a** figures **b** words.

  1 10^4 10^6 10^2 10^5 10^7 10^8

  2 $10^2 \times 5$ $10^3 \times 6$ $10^5 \times 8$ $10^4 \times 9$ $10^6 \times 3$

B Write in full in figures.

  1 367×10^2 $432 \cdot 5 \times 10^4$ $41 \cdot 29 \times 10^3$ $457 \cdot 6 \times 10^2$

       $11 \cdot 141 \times 10^5$ 2021×10^2 $6 \cdot 23 \times 10^4$ $0 \cdot 359 \times 10^5$

       2164×10^1 $5 \cdot 216 \times 10^3$ $90 \cdot 09 \times 10^2$ $8 \cdot 216 \times 10^4$

  2 $20 \cdot 47 \div 10^1$ $1\,141\,126 \div 10^3$ $173\,000\,000 \div 10^6$ $32 \cdot 7 \div 10^2$

       $2453 \div 10^2$ $16\,000 \div 10^4$ $473 \cdot 1 \div 10^2$ $66\,000 \div 10^2$

       $43\,200 \div 10^5$ $32\,150 \div 10^3$ $1\,200\,000 \div 10^6$ $39 \cdot 41 \div 10^3$

C 1 Complete the table.

	10^6	10^5	10^4	10^3	10^2	10^1	1
3541×10			3	5	4	1	0
4561×1000							
$4 \cdot 263 \times 1\,000\,000$							
$4\,732\,140 \div 10$							
$1\,150\,000 \div 10\,000$							
$6\,300\,000 \div 100\,000$							

D Write in full in figures.

  1 $10^3 \times 10^2$ $10^4 \times 10^2$ $10^6 \times 10^1$ $10^2 \times 10^2$

  2 $10^7 \div 10^2$ $10^9 \div 10^5$ $10^{10} \div 10^6$ $10^5 \div 10^3$

Base 2

A 1 What is the value of

2^1? 2^3? 2^6? 2^7? 2^5? 2^4? 2^2? 2^8?

2 Write as powers of 2.

16   128   1024   32   4   512   8   2   256   64

B 1 Write the value in denary numbers.

$2^3 \times 2^2$ $2^2 \times 2^4$ $2^3 \times 2^6$ $2^1 \times 2^5$ $2^3 \times 2^4$

2 $2^6 \div 2^4$ $2^5 \div 2^3$ $2^9 \div 2^6$ $2^8 \div 2^5$ $2^8 \div 2^7$

C Base 2

32	16	8	4	2	1	binary number	denary number
2^5	2^4	2^3	2^2	2^1	2^0		
		.	.	.			
.	.		.	.	.		
.		.	.		.		
.		.		.	.		
.	.		.	.			

1 Write down   **a** the binary numbers   **b** the denary numbers, represented by the dots on the chart.

2 Write these numbers as denary numbers.

11011_2 101010_2 111_2 1001_2 10001_2

D 1 Write as binary numbers.

63_{10} 47_{10} 29_{10} 35_{10} 18_{10} 7_{10}

2

10101_2	1111_2	11110_2	111_2	10010_2
1011_2	1010_2	10001_2	1010_2	11111_2
$+1110_2$	$+101_2$	$+1011_2$	$+11111_2$	$+1001_2$

3

1001_2	11101_2	10010_2	11110_2	101010_2
-110_2	-1001_2	-1001_2	-101_2	11110_2

Base 5 and base 3

A 1 What is the value of

5^3? 5^4? 5^2? 5^1?   five squared?   five cubed?

2 Write as power of 5

25   one hundred and twenty-five   twenty-five   5   125

B 1 Write out these denary numbers in base 5.

35_{10} 743_{10} 23_{10} 432_{10} 261_{10} 93_{10} 21_{10} 1041_{10}

2 Write out these base 5 numbers in base 10.

4302_5 2030_5 4101_5 332_5 2304_5 403_5 1214_5

C

$$4021_5 + 3021_5$$ $$2341_5 + 344_5$$ $$3244_5 + 444_5$$ $$4004_5 + 1023_5$$ $$3341_5 + 44_5$$

$$3241_5 - 2234_5$$ $$2030_5 - 434_5$$ $$4001_5 - 2441_5$$ $$2404_5 - 1040_5$$ $$1401_5 - 442_5$$

D 1 Write the value of

3^6 3^2 3^4 3^3 3^5 three cubed three squared

2 Write as powers of 3.

2187   27   243   81   3   729   9

3 Write the value in denary numbers.

$3^3 \times 3^2$ $3^2 \times 3^2$ $3^4 \times 3^2$ $3^6 \div 3^3$ $3^5 \div 3^2$ $3^4 \div 3^3$

E 1 Write these denary numbers in base 3.

87_{10} 26_{10} 150_{10} 56_{10} 21_{10} 102_{10} 19_{10} 253_{10}

2 Write these base 3 numbers in base 10.

2101_3 2220_3 1002_3 202_3 1212_3 2021_3

F

$$2112_3 + 1221_3$$ $$2002_3 - 2201_3$$ $$1212_3 - 222_3$$ $$2100_3 - 100_3$$ $$2211_3 - 122_3$$

Mixed bases

A **1** Write each of these denary numbers in **a** base 4 **b** base 6 **c** base 7 **d** base 8.

476_{10} 222_{10} 69_{10} 102_{10} 354_{10} 502_{10}

2 Write each of these numbers as denary numbers.

4342_5 3231_4 1205_6 63_7 176_8 2022_3 1101_2

B

4231_5	1001_4	5213_6	2012_3	101010_2
$+2022_5$	$+3213_4$	$+3101_6$	$+222_3$	$+11101_2$

6121_8	1212_3	1332_4	3241_5	101011_2
$+2010_8$	$+2020_3$	$+333_4$	$+1024_5$	$+111_2$

3121_4	2414_5	1217_8	2000_3	1151_6
-303_4	-1441_5	-613_8	-1212_3	-505_6

101110_2	3143_5	2022_3	3031_4	611_7
-111_2	-244_5	-222_3	-2203_4	-266_7

C Write which base has been used in these sums.

1

2112	2411	2173	10101	3231
+3023	+2222	+2046	+1111	+1021
11201	10133	4219	100100	10312

2

1001	3200	1010	1365	2121
-111	-322	-121	-721	-132
10	2212	112	644	1434

Capacity

A Complete

1 2471 ml =   l   3016 ml =   l   743 ml =   l

    76 ml =   l   126 ml =   l   2354 ml =   l

2 2·436 l =   ml   0·125 l =   ml   0·637 l =   ml

   0·047 l =   ml   2·071 ml =   ml   0·007 l =   ml

3   500 ml =   l   400 ml =   l   450 ml =   l

    750 ml =   l   850 ml =   l   350 ml =   l

   4270 ml =   l   3680 ml =   l   1550 ml =   l

   6150 ml =   l   2250 ml =   l   10 950 ml =   l

4 $4\frac{2}{5}$ l =   ml $6\frac{1}{4}$ l =   ml $\frac{7}{10}$ l =   ml

   $\frac{7}{20}$ l =   ml $1\frac{4}{5}$ l =   ml $\frac{9}{25}$ l =   ml

   $5\frac{3}{4}$ l =   ml $9\frac{239}{250}$ l =   ml $\frac{113}{250}$ l =   ml

   $2\frac{3}{10}$ l =   ml $\frac{9}{10}$ l =   ml $12\frac{3}{5}$ l =   ml

5 Use the signs > or < to complete

   0·38 l   38 ml | 4·06 l   4600 ml | $1\frac{3}{5}$ l   1500 ml

   $3\frac{3}{10}$ l   3030 ml | $9\frac{7}{20}$ l   9·035 ml | 0·035 l   350 ml

B **1** 2·36 l + 575 ml + $\frac{1}{2}$ l =   l   4·5 l + $6\frac{1}{4}$ l + 2 l 76 ml =   l

   5·06 l + 0·027 l + $\frac{3}{4}$ l =   l   19·5 l + $6\frac{7}{10}$ l + 5420 ml =   l

2   6·257 l − $5\frac{3}{10}$ l =   ml $12\frac{1}{2}$ l − 7396 ml =   l

   8 l 27 ml − 7 l 54 ml =   ml   21 l 16 ml − 9·239 l =   l

3   47·213 l × 6 =   l   3 l 60 ml × 5 =   l

   41 271 ml × 9 =   l $7\frac{9}{25}$ l × 8 =   l

4   12·864 l ÷ 4 =   l $51\frac{3}{4}$ l ÷ 9 =   l

   3 l 475 ml ÷ 5 =   l   515·252 l ÷ 12 =   l

Mass

A 1 Write as decimal fractions.

$2\frac{3}{4}$ kg $1\frac{4}{5}$ kg $\frac{7}{10}$ kg $\frac{9}{20}$ kg $3\frac{13}{25}$ kg $6\frac{27}{1000}$ kg

$3\frac{3}{100}$ kg $8\frac{1}{4}$ kg $\frac{1}{2}$ kg $\frac{11}{20}$ kg $1\frac{3}{5}$ kg $6\frac{13}{1000}$ kg

2 Write as vulgar fractions.

4·750 kg   0·850 kg   0·950 kg   3·4 kg   4·7 kg

0·925 kg   0·050 kg   4·45 kg   9·3 kg   0·25 kg

3 Which of these weights are greater than $\frac{1}{2}$ kg?

475 g   620 g   510 g   0·375 kg   0·601 kg   0·356 kg

4 Which of these weights are less than $\frac{3}{4}$ tonne?

675 kg   1046 kg   0·6 t   0·76 t   432 kg   0·78 t

5 Write these weights in order of size — smallest first.

1 t   1200 kg   2500 g   750 kg   0·75 kg   2·524 kg

6 Write these weights in tonnes and kilograms.

$3\frac{3}{4}$ t   6·9 t   11·75 t   6·85 t $8\frac{7}{10}$ t $5\frac{4}{5}$ t

7 Write these weights in tonnes.

6 t 27 kg   11 t 9 kg   4 t 263 kg   347 kg   62 kg

B Give your answers to the following as decimal fractions of tonnes or kilograms.

1   4·25 t + $2\frac{1}{2}$ t + 3472 kg $3\frac{1}{2}$ t + 704 kg + 925 kg

     8 kg 40 g + 800 g + 6 kg 50 g   1900 g + 700 g + 36·56 kg

2 27·35 kg − $25\frac{3}{4}$ kg   9·340 kg − 8 kg 709 g

     342 t − 276 t 78 kg $4\frac{1}{2}$ kg − 3124 g

3   7 kg 164 g × 7 $14\frac{1}{2}$ t × 12   6 kg 507 g × 8   35 t 176 kg × 10

4   35·208 t ÷ 9 $72\frac{3}{4}$ kg ÷ 6   111 t 5 kg ÷ 5   30 kg 800 g ÷ 7

Length

A 1 Write as kilometres.

3 km 27 m   21 km 345 m   432 m   3400 cm   12 000 mm

5300 cm   6 km 5 m   2475 m   26 m   12 km 35 m

2 Write as metres.

6 m 26 cm   5 m 6 cm   21 m 27 mm   45 mm   96 mm

12 m 175 mm   16 m 7 cm   2141 mm   21 m 6 mm   7 mm

3 Write as decimals.

$6\frac{1}{4}$ km $11\frac{1}{2}$ km $17\frac{3}{4}$ km $3\frac{7}{10}$ km $2\frac{4}{5}$ km $\frac{11}{20}$ km

$8\frac{3}{5}$ m $12\frac{3}{10}$ m $2\frac{7}{20}$ m $12\frac{3}{4}$ m $11\frac{9}{20}$ m $14\frac{9}{10}$ m

4 Write as vulgar fractions.

12·5 km   26·75 km   32·7 km   45·05 km   16·015 km

9·6 m   13·45 m   0·25 m   18·55 m   0·95 m

5 Write as kilometres and metres.

14·75 km   6·234 km   8·632 km   12·275 km   12·7 km

6·45 km   10·035 km $11\frac{4}{5}$ km $8\frac{9}{10}$ km   9·6 km

B 1   2 km 40 m + 2·725 km + 3·2 km =   km

$2\frac{3}{4}$ km + 3·55 km + 732 m =   km

5 cm 8 mm + 10 cm 9 mm + 17 cm =   cm   mm

3·6 cm + 9 mm + 6·9 cm =   cm

2   73 cm − 635 mm =   cm   106 km − 7·432 km =   km

12·9 m − 16·2 cm =   m $115\frac{3}{4}$ km − 945 m =   km

3   3 m 75 cm × 4 =   m   4·125 cm × 6 =   cm

127 cm 7 mm × 11 =   cm   mm   73 m 9 mm × 9 =   m   mm

14·325 km × 7 =   km   0·375 m × 5 =   m

4 196 cm 5 mm ÷ 5 =   cm $325\frac{1}{2}$ m ÷ 7 =   m

2·376 km ÷ 6 =   km   698·4 cm ÷ 8 =   cm

41 m 4 cm ÷ 9 =   m   45 m 4 mm ÷ 4 =   m

Averages

A Find the average of each set of numbers.

1	3·24	4·60	2·71	9·81	
2	21·21	9·21	4·30	2·27	6·16
3	6·26	19·46	23·75	13·44	12·71	19·54
4	2745	5621	4220	3174	
5	227 432	347 609	476 540		

B

1 The average weight of nine boys was 38·5 kg. What was their total weight?

2 The average cost of seven articles was £2·25. What was the total cost?

3 On a touring holiday which lasted 14 days, the average distance covered each day was 48 km. What was the total distance travelled?

4 A milkman delivered 674 l of milk each day. If he made no deliveries on Sunday, how much milk did he deliver in one week?

5 The average height of six boys was 152 cm. The total height of five of the boys was 765 cm, so how tall was the other boy?

6 Eight parcels weigh 760 g. The weights of seven of the parcels are 93 g, 87 g, 91 g, 96 g, 98 g, 89 g, 90 g.
a What does the other parcel weigh?   b How much more than the average weight does this parcel weigh?

7 The average spending money of five children is 38p. The spending money of four of the children is 60p, 45p, 35p and 20p. Find   a the total spending money   b the spending money of the other child.

Metric measures—problems

1 A box full of packets weighs 33 kg. If the box weighs $1\frac{1}{2}$ kg, how many 350 g packets does it hold?

2 Find the total length of four remnants of material measuring 9·6 cm, 19·27 cm, 26·51 cm and 32·75 cm.

3 How much orange squash is needed to fill 24 bottles each holding 725 ml?

4 A storage tank holds 10 000 litres of petrol. 3670 l is sold on Monday and 4165 l on Tuesday. How much is left in the tank?

5 A car is bought having been driven 11 345·7 km. After 1 year it has gone 19 462·9 km. What distance was covered in the first year?

6 One loaded lorry weighs 4 t 29 kg. Another weighs 3 t 125 kg. What is the difference in weight?

7 A school kitchen uses 120 kg of potatoes each day. How many kilograms are used in four weeks?

8 How many 250 ml cartons can be filled from 2400 l?

9 36 poles are fixed 1·75 m apart. How much wire is required to link them?

10 The daily deliveries of milk to a school are 290 l, 280 l, 325 l, 350 l, 375 l. How much is delivered in the week?

11 Four salesmen travel the following distances in a year: 12 475 km, 16 954 km, 18 627 km and 20 432 km. What was the average distance travelled?

12 A lorry carried 13 t 75 kg on the first day, 14 t 17 kg on the second day and 16 t 96 kg on the third day. What was the total weight for the three days?

Area and perimeter

A   Find   **a** the perimeter in mm   **b** the area in mm²

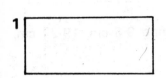

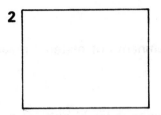

B   Find the perimeter of rectangles which measure

    a 20·4 cm by 7 cm   **b** 36·4 mm by 15 mm   **c** 9 m × 12·6 m

    d 12·7 cm by 8·3 cm   **e** 914 mm by 131 mm   **f** 11·6 m × 15·3 m

C   Complete the table of measurements of rectangles.

length	15 cm	16 cm			25 cm	25 cm	
width	19 cm		12 cm	18 cm		34 cm	23 cm
perimeter			62 cm		80 cm		
area		176 cm²		306 cm²			598 cm²

D   Find   **a** the perimeter   **b** the area.

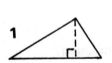

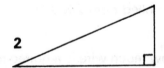

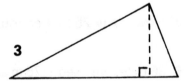

E   Find the area of triangles which measure

base	height		base	height
17 cm	15 cm		23·5 cm	12 cm
22 cm	20 cm		9·5 m	7 m
75 mm	27 mm		10·75 cm	14 cm

F   Complete this table of measurements of triangles.

base	12 cm	15 cm	12 cm		24 cm	30·5 cm	
height		16 cm		15 cm	9 cm		32 cm
area	60 cm²		72 cm²	112·5 cm²		122 cm²	160 cm²

Area

Find the area of the unshaded parts.

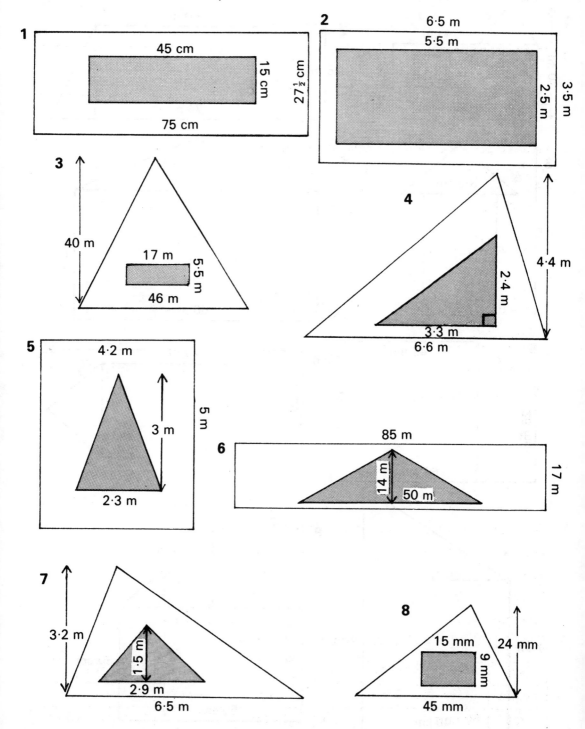

1
45 cm
15 cm
27½ cm
75 cm

2
6·5 m
5·5 m
3·5 m
2·5 m

3
40 m
17 m
5·5 m
46 m

4
4·4 m
2·4 m
3·3 m
6·6 m

5
4·2 m
3 m
5 m
2·3 m

6
85 m
14 m
50 m
17 m

7
3·2 m
1·5 m
2·9 m
6·5 m

8
15 mm
24 mm
9 mm
45 mm

Area

Find the total area of each of these shapes.

1

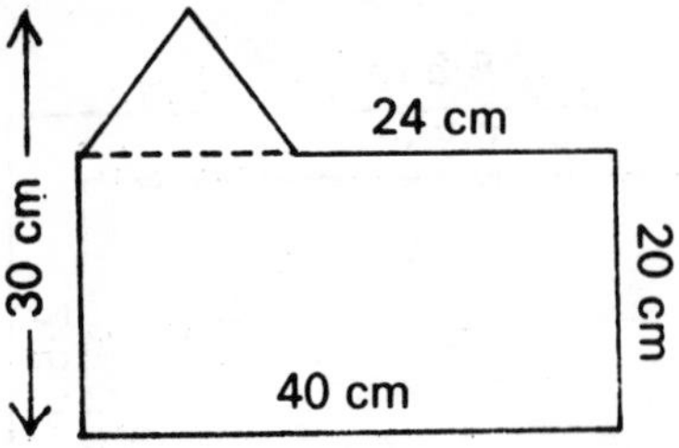

2

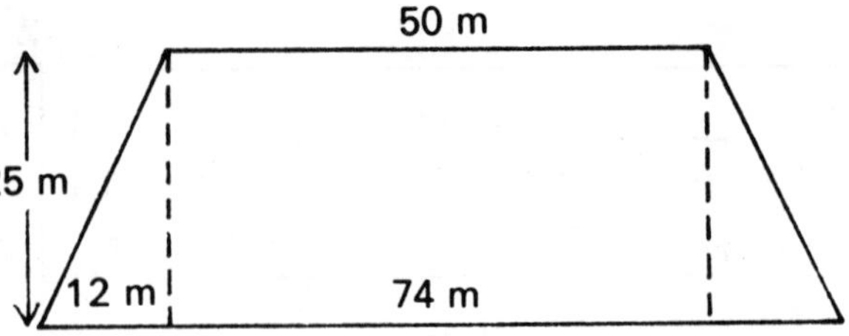

3

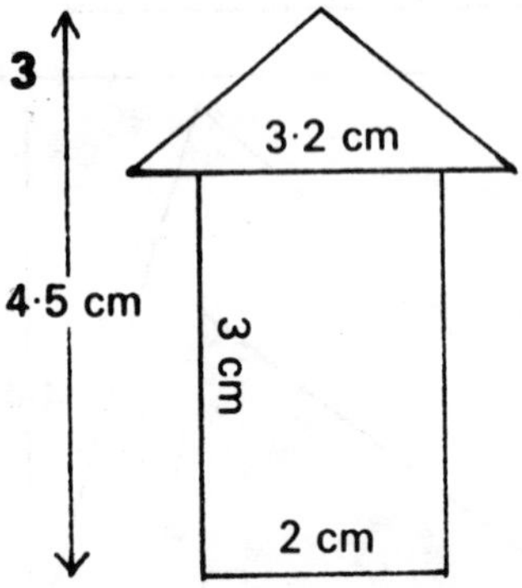

4

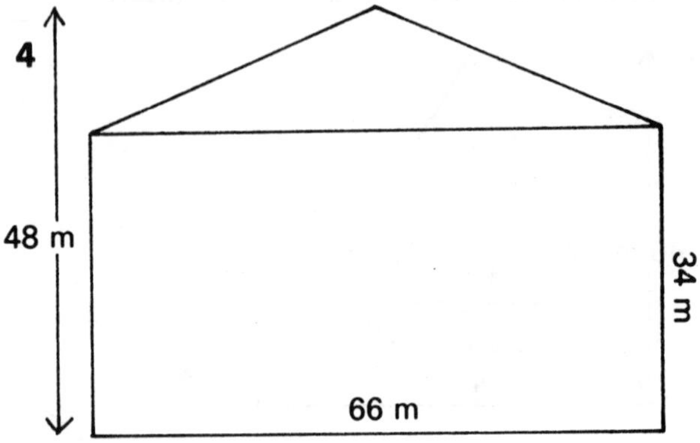

5

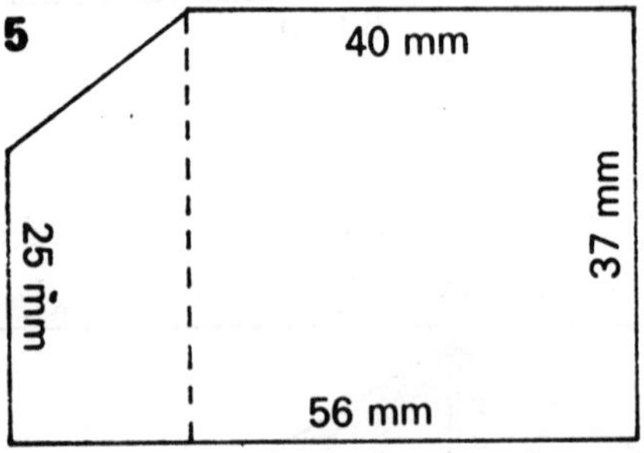

6

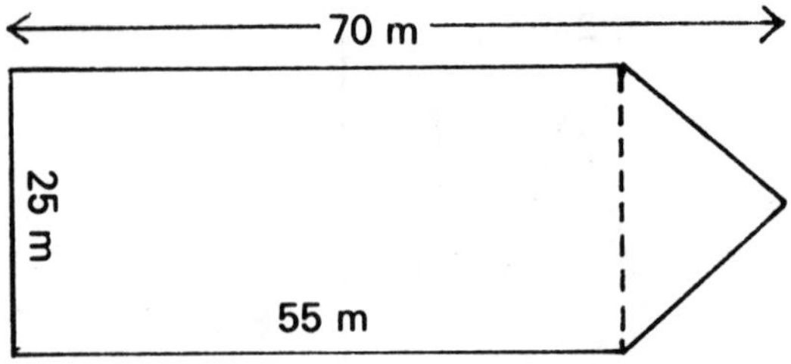

7

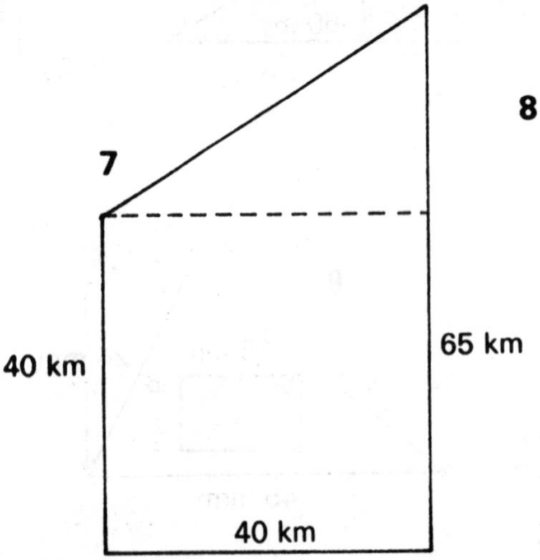

8

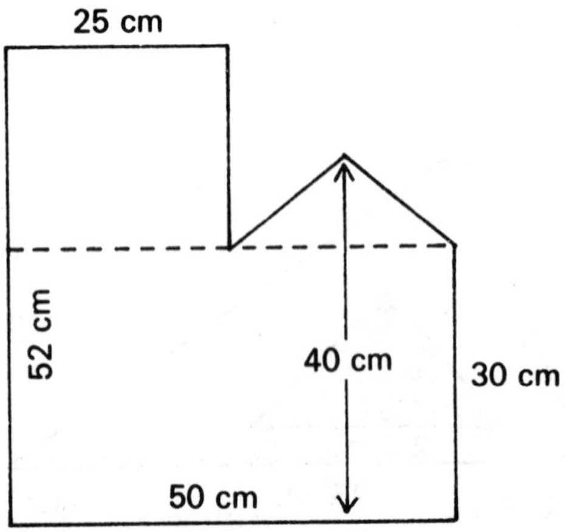

Circumference of circles

A 1 Draw circles with a radius of

2 cm	$5\frac{1}{2}$ cm	3 cm	$4\frac{1}{2}$ cm	$1\frac{1}{2}$ cm
2·4 cm	3·2 cm	2·9 cm	4·4 cm	1·8 cm

2 Draw circles with a diameter of

5·2 cm	10 cm	$7\frac{1}{2}$ cm	8·5 cm	11 cm	6·8 cm

B Give the radius when the diameter is

1 11·2 m   9·6 cm   12·7 m   15·2 m   16·9 cm   13·5 cm

2 Give the diameter when the radius is

$7\frac{3}{4}$ cm $15\frac{1}{2}$ cm $2\frac{1}{4}$ m $6\frac{7}{10}$ m $4\frac{3}{5}$ cm $12\frac{1}{2}$ m

C 1 Circumference of a circle = $2\pi r$

Using $3\frac{1}{7}$ as the value of π, find the circumference if the radius is

$2\frac{3}{4}$ cm $6\frac{3}{4}$ cm $4\frac{1}{2}$ cm   9 cm $12\frac{1}{2}$ cm $5\frac{1}{2}$ cm

2 Circumference of a circle = πd

Using $3\frac{1}{7}$ as the value of π, find the circumference if the diameter is

7 cm $6\frac{1}{2}$ cm   15 cm   19 cm $7\frac{3}{4}$ cm $14\frac{1}{2}$ cm

D 1 Using π as 3·14, find the circumference when the radius is

2·7 m   3·4 cm   6·9 m   18·5 cm   16·7 cm

2 Using π as 3·14, find the circumference when the diameter is

29·8 m   47·2 cm   35·6 cm   18·5 m   0·75 m

Area of circles

A Area of a circle $= \pi r^2$. Use $3\frac{1}{7}$ as the value of π.

1 Find the area of the circle if the radius is

  7 cm   14 cm   28 cm   35 cm $5\frac{1}{4}$ cm $7\frac{7}{8}$ cm

2 Find the area of a circle if the diameter is

  $3\frac{1}{2}$ cm $10\frac{1}{2}$ cm   21 cm $24\frac{1}{2}$ cm $31\frac{1}{2}$ cm   35 cm

B Use 3·14 as the value of π.

1 Find the area of the circle when the radius is

  3 cm   9 cm   6 cm   11 cm   4 cm   7 cm

2 Find the area of the circle if the diameter is

  28 cm   24 cm   36 cm

  22 cm   48 cm   10 cm

C 1 Complete the table using 3·14 as the value of π.

diameter (in cm)	12·8					1·6	
radius (in cm)		5·1			1·4		
circumference (in cm)			28·26				50·24
area (in cm²)				78·5			

2 Find the area and perimeter of these shapes.

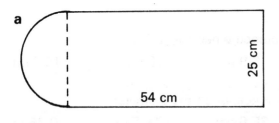

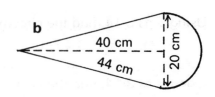

Volume of cubes and cuboids

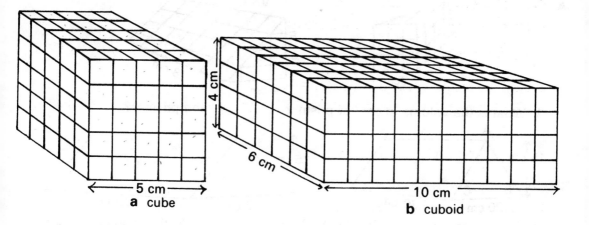

a cube — 5 cm, 4 cm

b cuboid — 6 cm, 10 cm

A **1** What is the volume of cube **a** in cm³?

2 Complete these tables of volumes of cubes, using the formula $v = l \times b \times h$.

length of side	4 cm	6 cm	11 cm	9 cm	10 cm	$4\frac{1}{2}$ cm
volume						

length of side	$6\frac{1}{2}$ cm	$10\frac{1}{2}$ cm	$11\frac{1}{2}$ cm	$12\frac{1}{2}$ cm	$8\frac{1}{2}$ cm
volume					

B **1** What is the volume of the cuboid **b** above in cm³?

2 Complete this table of volumes of cuboids, using the formula $v = l \times b \times h$

length	7 cm	$10\frac{1}{2}$ cm	$15\frac{1}{2}$ cm	8 cm	22 cm	$12\frac{1}{2}$ cm	15 cm
breadth	$4\frac{1}{2}$ cm	6 cm	$3\frac{1}{2}$ cm	$4\frac{1}{2}$ cm	$3\frac{1}{2}$ cm	10 cm	8 cm
height	4 cm	2 cm	4 cm	$2\frac{1}{2}$ cm	$2\frac{1}{4}$ cm	$2\frac{1}{2}$ cm	$3\frac{1}{2}$ cm
volume							

3 Write the formula used to find

a length when the breadth, height and volume are known.

b breadth when the length, height and volume are known.

c height when the breadth, length and volume are known.

Volume—triangular prisms and cylinders

A

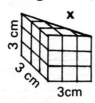

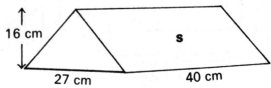

1 What is the volume in cm³ of prism **x** and prism **y**?

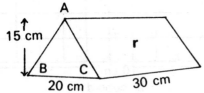

2 Find **a** the area of triangle ABC in **r** **b** the volume of prism **r**.

3 Find the volume of prism **s**.

4 Find the volume of the triangular prisms in the table. Remember

$$v = b \times \tfrac{1}{2} \text{ perpendicular ht} \times l$$

triangular prism	a	b	c	d	e	f	g	h	i	j
base (b) in cm	6	9	10	15	23	25	35	50	28	30
perpendicular height (ht) in cm	5	4½	7	9½	12	10	16	15	20	11
length (l) in cm	15	10	20	15	25	16	12	30	15	25
volume (v) in cm³										

B

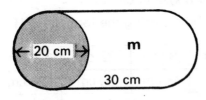

1 Find **a** the area of the shaded part of **m**, **b** the volume of the cylinder **m**.   Use $\frac{22}{7}$ as the value of π.

2 Find the volume of cylinder **n** in the same way.

3 Use $\pi r^2 l$ to find the volume of these cylinders. Use 3·14 as the value of π.

cylinder	a	b	c	d	e	f
radius (r) in cm	4	7	3	9	2	6
length (l) in cm	10	20	5	12	8	30
volume (v) in cm³						

Volume — assorted shapes

Find the volume of these shapes.

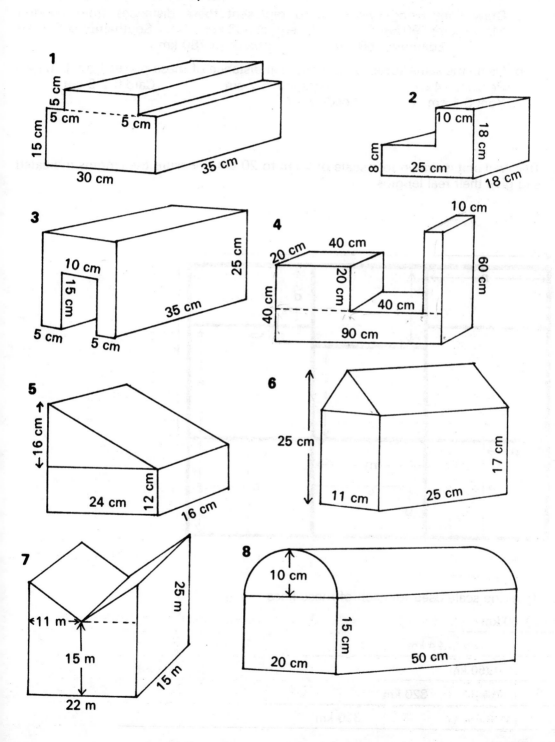

1
5 cm
5 cm
5 cm
5 cm
15 cm
35 cm
30 cm

2
10 cm
18 cm
8 cm
25 cm
18 cm

3
10 cm
15 cm
25 cm
35 cm
5 cm
5 cm

4
10 cm
20 cm
40 cm
20 cm
40 cm
40 cm
60 cm
90 cm

5
16 cm
24 cm
12 cm
16 cm

6
25 cm
11 cm
25 cm
17 cm

7
25 m
11 m
15 m
15 m
22 m

8
10 cm
15 cm
20 cm
50 cm

Scale drawing

A 1 A map has a scale of 1 mm to 10 km.

a Draw lines using this scale to represent these distances from London.
Manchester 290 km   Liverpool 300 km   Southampton 250 km
Edinburgh 600 km   Aberdeen 780 km

b Using the same scale, what is the real distance of these places from London?
Penzance 4·5 cm   Glasgow 6·2 cm   Cardiff 2·5 cm
York 3·1 cm   Leeds 3 cm

B This wall unit is drawn to a scale of 1 cm to 20 cm. Measure the lengths indicated and give their real lengths.

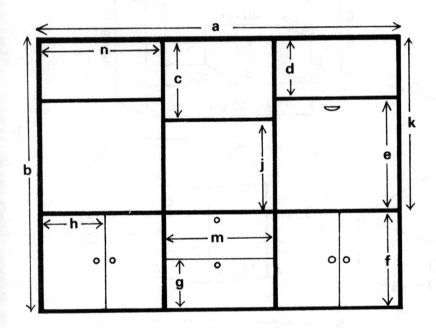

C Give the scale used for each of these lines.

60 km
_____

14 km
_____

250 km
_____

320 km
_____

300 km
_____

Scale drawing

A This is a sketch of an allotment. Draw it accurately to a scale of 0·2 cm to 1 m.

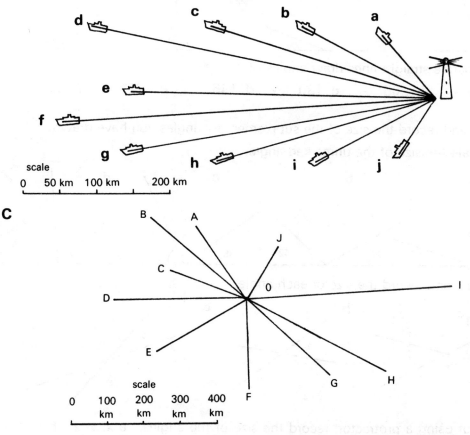

B Find out how far each ship is from the lighthouse.

C

1 A, B, C, D, E, F, G, H, I, J are airports. How far is each airport from o?

2 How far would each distance be if the scale of the map was

a 1 cm to 50 km? b 1 cm to 20 km? c 1 cm to 40 km? d 1 cm to 200 km?

Angles

A 1 Use a protractor to draw these angles.

62°	27°	54°	83°	35°	75°	45°	15°
95°	125°	160°	135°	170°	140°	115°	110°

2 Measure and record the two angles on each line.

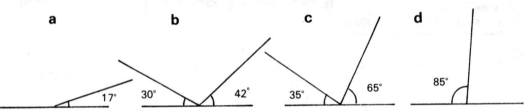

a   b   c   d

e   f   g   h

3 On separate straight lines draw angles of

    a 35°   **b** 65°   **c** 130°   **d** 145°   **e** 25°   **f** 55°

Measure and record the size of the supplementary angles you have drawn.

4 Calculate the size of the unmarked angle.

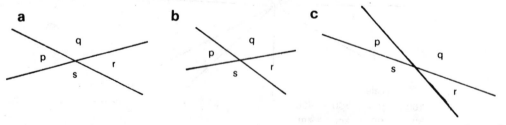

a   b   c   d

17°   30°   42°   35°   65°   85°

B 1 Measure and record the size of each angle.

a   b   c

2 Without using a protractor, record the size of the angles   **a** x, y, z   **b** a, b, c
   c r, s, t.

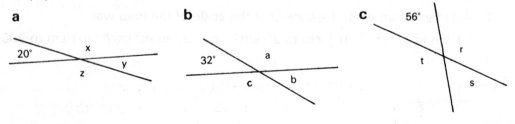

a   b   c

20°   x   y   z   32°   a   c   b   56°   r   t   s

Angles in triangles and quadrilaterals

A 1 Measure and record the size of the angles in each of these triangles.

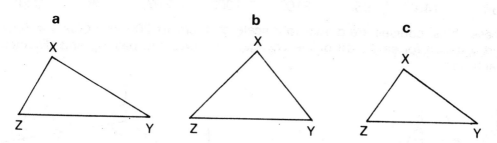

a   b   c

2 a On a base line AB draw triangles with the following base angles.

30° 40°	75° 50°	25° 80°	90° 45°	65° 30°
105° 45°	125° 20°	120° 35°	55° 60°	70° 60°

b Measure and record the unknown angle in each triangle.

3 Without using a protractor, calculate the size of the missing angle in these triangles.

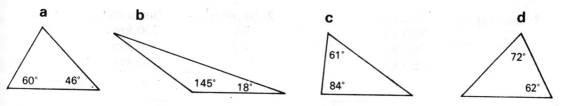

a   b   c   d

B 1 Measure and record the size of the angles in each of these quadrilaterals.

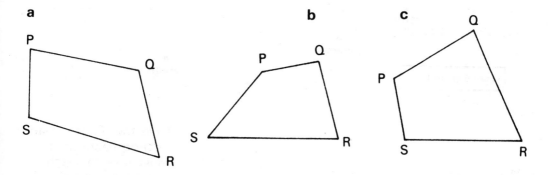

a   b   c

2 Draw quadrilaterals using the following sets of three angles, then measure and record the unknown angle.

75° 110° 95°	45° 120° 70°	50° 60° 115°
30° 130° 150°	55° 75° 125°	80° 95° 100°

3 Calculate the size of the missing angle in these quadrilaterals.

   a 105° 95° 60°   **b** 150° 145° 45°   **c** 200° 70° 60°

Bearings

A Plot the following bearings.

    230°   140°   85°   310°   100°   210°   75°   330°

B These ships' courses are drawn to a scale of 1 cm to 200 km. Give the bearing and distance for each part of the voyage, then give the bearing and distance to reach home.

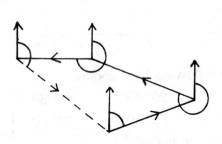 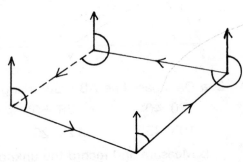

C Plot these courses and then give bearing and distance back to base (scale 1 cm to 100 km).

1 bearing	distance		**2** bearing	distance
70°	350 km		265°	300 km
350°	250 km		20°	300 km
270°	550 km		110°	550 km

D

                           ☐• cinema   ☐• school

         • Peter

                • Freda

scale 5 cm to 1 km

               • Alan   • Joan

             John   • Pam
             •

Give the approximate bearing each child must take to reach **a** school **b** the cinema. How far does each child live from **a** school **b** the cinema?

24 h times

A 1 The clocks below show times after 12 noon. Record the pm times shown **a** in words
    b in figures only.

(i)   (ii)   (iii)    (iv) 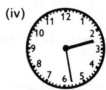   (v)

2 Record the times shown as 24 h clock times.

B (i) `0 6 4 2`   (ii) `2 1 1 7`   (iii) `1 9 2 0`   (iv) `0 2 0 3`   (v) `1 5 4 5`

1 Record the times shown on these digital clocks as **a** 24 h clock times **b** 12 h
clock times.

2 Give the difference in h and min between clocks

(i) and (iv)	(ii) and (iii)	(iii) and (iv)
(iv) and (v)	(i) and (iii)	(ii) and (iv)
(iii) and (v)	(i) and (v)	(ii) and (v)
(i) and (ii)		

3 How many hours and minutes must pass before each clock shows midnight?

C 1 Rewrite these times in 24 h clock times.

    2·24 am   3·45 pm   9·25 pm   6·45 am   11·20 pm   10·30 am   12·20 pm

    1·18 pm   4·32 am   8·52 am   5·40 pm   2·26 am   7·12 pm   5·54 pm

2 Rewrite these times in 12 h clock times.

    12·16   14·35   07·19   06·45   21·20   23·50

    05·19   22·51   03·15   19·26   04·16   20·48

D Make the times shown in **C1** and **C2** **a** 25 min later **b** 45 min later **c** 1 h 30 min
later **d** 20 min earlier **e** 40 min earlier **f** 1 h 15 min earlier.

Timetables

A 1 Buses leave Manchester for Liverpool every forty minutes. Give the departure times from Manchester from 09·00 h to 15·00 h.

2 The journey takes 1 h 15 min. Give the arrival times at Liverpool.

3 The bus crew have a quarter of an hour rest before starting the return journey. Give the departure time for each bus from Liverpool.

4 Give the arrival times at Manchester.

B 1 Boat trips on the river at Chester commence at 09·15. Boats leave at thirty minute intervals for a forty minute sail. Complete this timetable for one of the boats.

depart	09·15	10·15							
arrive	09·55								

2 How many trips does the boat make each day?

3 What time does the last boat sail?

4 A schoolparty has to leave Chester at 15·30. What is the latest time they can take a boat trip?

5 The boat holds 72 people. If it is full on each trip how many people will be carried in one day?

6 On a certain day, one third of the passengers carried were children. If the fare is 40p per adult and 20p per child how much money was taken on this day?

C A miniature railway runs twenty minute round trips commencing at 09·00 until 12·15. If there is a 5 minute wait at the end of each trip, draw up the railway timetable for the train.

Speed

A A car travels at an average speed of 60 km/h.

1 How far will it travel in

   a 5 h?   **b** 6·5 h?   **c** 8·25 h?   **d** 2·75 h?

   e 4·3 h?   **f** 2 h 12 min?   **g** 4 h 35 min?   **h** 1 h 50 min?

2 How long will it take to travel

   a 250 km?   **b** 320 km?   **c** 262 km?   **d** 455 km?   **e** 610 km?

B A coach travels 4800 km.

1 How many hours was the coach driven at an average speed of

   a 20 km/h?   **b** 50 km/h?   **c** 100 km/h?   **d** 30 km/h?

   e 80 km/h?   **f** 150 km/h?   **g** 60 km/h?   **h** 120 km/h?

2 At what speed did the coach travel if it was driven for

   a 50 h?   **b** 75 h?   **c** 60 h?   **d** 40 h?   **e** 80 h?

C 1 Convert to km/h.

   a 5·5 km in 12 min   **b** 4·25 km in 5 min   **c** 35 km in 2 min

   d 12·25 km in 4 min   **e** 10·5 km in $1\frac{1}{2}$ min   **f** 20·5 km in 20 min

2 Convert to m/s.

   a 0·3 km in $\frac{1}{2}$ min   **b** 0·6 km in $\frac{1}{4}$ min   **c** 0·1 km in $\frac{1}{6}$ min

   d 0·4 km in $\frac{2}{3}$ min   **e** 0·9 km in $\frac{3}{4}$ min   **f** 0·3 km in $\frac{5}{6}$ min

3 Convert to km/h.

   a 100 m/s   **b** 230 m/s   **c** 192 m/s

   d 150 m/s   **e** 210 m/s   **f** 80 m/s

4 Convert to m/s.

   a 180 km/h   **b** 54 km/h   **c** 126 km/h

   d 162 km/h   **e** 27 km/h   **f** 252 km/h

Speed

A

flight	distance	time	av. speed
a	3500 km	$3\frac{1}{2}$ h	
b	2400 km	$2\frac{1}{2}$ h	
c		3 h 20 min	1200 km/h
d	2240 km	2 h 40 min	
e	3680 km		960 km/h
f	4400 km	$5\frac{1}{2}$ h	

1 Copy and complete this table of air flights.

2 Which two planes travel at the same speed?

3 List the planes in order of speed — fastest first.

B The speed of very fast aircraft is sometimes measured in Mach numbers. Mach 1 is 1200 km/h.

1 Convert these Mach numbers to km/h.

Mach 2   Mach 3   Mach 4   Mach 5   Mach 6

Mach 2·5   Mach 4·75   Mach 3·2   Mach 4·1   Mach 6·3

2 Convert these km/h to Mach numbers.

7440 km/h   2880 km/h   1980 km/h   5700 km/h

6300 km/h   3960 km/h   2850 km/h   1320 km/h

Graphs — revision

A

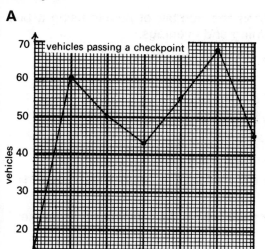

1 Which day has

   a most   **b** least vehicles?

2 What is the difference between the highest and lowest totals?

3 What was the average number of vehicles per day?

4 On which day was the total 25% of Monday's total?

5 On which day was the total

   a $\frac{3}{4}$ **b** $\frac{5}{6}$

   of Monday's total?

6 Which day's total was 3 times that of Sunday?

7 How many totals were more than the average?

8 How many totals were less than average?

B Draw the graph which shows the number of fine days each month in one year. Check your graph with the teacher.

Jan	Feb	Mar	Apr	May	June	July	Aug	Sept	Oct	Nov	Dec
7	15	17	18	25	26	20	19	22	20	13	9

C

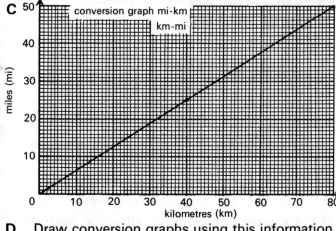

Change to kilometres

5 mi	15 mi	30 mi	40 mi

$17\frac{1}{2}$ mi	$27\frac{1}{2}$ mi	$42\frac{1}{2}$ mi	$22\frac{1}{2}$ mi

Change to miles

24 km	48 km	32 km	56 km

20 km	52 km	12 km	60 km

D Draw conversion graphs using this information. Check them with the teacher.

kilograms	1	4	7	old pence	2·4	24	36
pounds	2·2	8·8	15·4	new pence	1	10	15

Graphs—comparison graphs

A

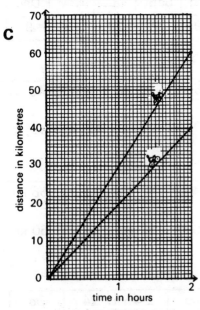

The graph shows the number of people using a bus station morning and evenings.

1 How many travelled each morning?

2 How many travelled each evening?

3 How many travelled on the 7 mornings altogether?

4 How many travelled on the 7 evenings altogether?

5 What is the difference in these totals?

6 Which mornings did the total exceed $3\frac{1}{2}$ thousand?

B Draw a graph to record this information. Check your graph with the teacher.

midday	8°C	4°C	9°C	6°C	4°C	0°C	7°C
midnight	3°C	−4°C	2°C	−1°C	−2°C	−5°C	3°C
day	Sun	Mon	Tue	Wed	Thurs	Fri	Sat

C

The graph shows a comparison between the distances travelled by a cyclist and scooter driver.

1 What is the speed in km/h of

  a the cyclist?   **b** the scooter?

2 How far has each travelled after

  a $\frac{1}{4}$ h?   **b** $\frac{1}{2}$ h?
  c $1\frac{1}{4}$ h?   **d** $1\frac{1}{2}$ h?
  e $1\frac{3}{4}$ h?

3 How much farther has the scooter travelled after

  a 12 min?   **b** 21 min?
  c 39 min?   **d** 1 h 9 min?
  e 1 h 21 min?   **f** 1 h 57 min?

4 If the scooter breaks down after one hour, how long would it take the cyclist to catch up?

D Draw a graph to compare these speeds — 80 km/h and 60 km/h. Check your graph with the teacher.

Co-ordinates

A 1

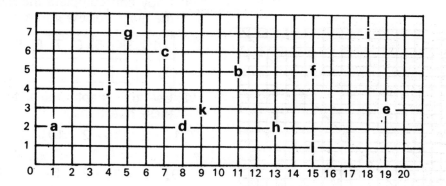

Write the co-ordinates of the points **a** to **l**.

2 On a piece of squared paper plot the following co-ordinates listing the points **a** to **l**.

a (0, 1)   **b** (2, 7)   **c** (3, 6)   **d** (4, 4)   **e** (6, 7)   **f** (9, 5)

g (2, 8)   **h** (5, 3)   **i** (4, 5)   **j** (9, 2)   **k** (7, 4)   **l** (8, 3)

Check your result with the teacher.

B

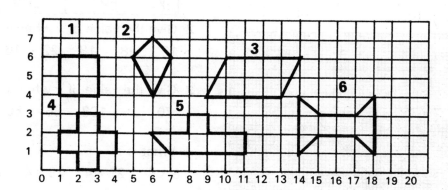

1 List the co-ordinates needed to plot each shape. Check your answers with the teacher.

2 On a piece of squared paper plot these co-ordinates. They will give five letters to make a word.

a (2, 1) (2, 5) (1, 5) (1, 6) (4, 6) (4, 5) (3, 5) (3, 1)

b (5, 1) (5, 6) (6, 6) (6, 4) (7, 4) (7, 6) (8, 6) (8, 1) (7, 1) (7, 3) (6, 3) (6, 1)

c (9, 1) (9, 6) (10, 6) (10, 1)

d (11, 1) (11, 6) (12, 6) (13, 4) (13, 6) (14, 6) (14, 1) (13, 1) (12, 3) (12, 1)

e (15, 1) (15, 6) (16, 6) (16, 4) (17, 6) (18, 6) (17, 4) (17, 3) (18, 1) (17, 1) (16, 3) (16, 1)

Co-ordinates

A

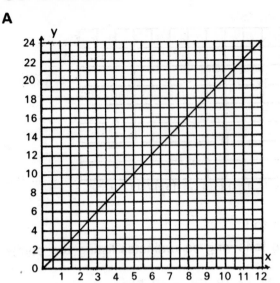

1 Copy and complete the table. Use the graph for the information.

x	1	2	3	4	5	6	7	8	9	10	11	12
y												

2 Use the graph again to answer these questions.

$1\frac{1}{2} \times 2$ $7\frac{1}{2} \times 2$ $10\frac{1}{2} \times 2$ $6\frac{1}{2} \times 2$

$9\frac{1}{2} \times 2$ $3\frac{1}{2} \times 2$ $5\frac{1}{2} \times 2$ $11\frac{1}{2} \times 2$

$15 \div 2$ $21 \div 2$ 23×2 $9 \div 2$

$5 \div 2$ $13 \div 2$ $17 \div 2$ $19 \div 2$

B **1** Copy and complete the table. Use the graph for the information.

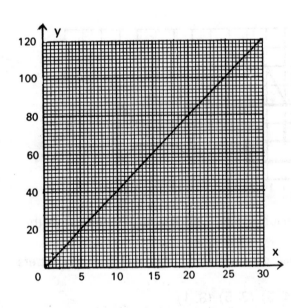

x	5		15	20		30
y		40			100	

2 Give the value of y when x is

12   28   18   22   16   26

3 Give the value of x when y is

70   36   108   86   50   28

4 What is

9×4 21×4 29×4 16×4

13×4 28×4 19×4 11×4

$108 \div 4$ $92 \div 4$ $76 \div 4$

$116 \div 4$ $56 \div 4$ $104 \div 4$

C Complete these tables, then draw the graph to show the relationship between x and y. Check your graphs with the teacher.

x	1	2	5	10	15	20
y	8	16	40	80	120	160

x	1	2	5	10	15	20
y	7	14	35	70	105	140

Sets — revision

A 1 Write out the missing members of each set.

$V = \{3, 6, 9, 12, \quad\quad 24, 27, 30\}$ $X = \{1, 4, 9, 16, \quad\quad 64, 81\}$
   three missing members   three missing members

$T = \{1, 2, 3, 4, \quad 8, 9, 10\}$ $Z = \{12, 24, 36, \quad\quad 108, 120\}$
   three missing members   five missing members

2 Name the above sets. Check answers with the teacher.

B Write out four infinite sets, eg $B = \{5, 10, 15, 20, 25 \ldots\}$. Check answers with the teacher.

C $S = \{$banana, orange, cabbage, pea, pear, carrot, bean$\}$. Write in full these subsets of S.

$T = \{$fruits$\}$

$R = \{$vegetables$\}$

$U = \{$things beginning with p$\}$

$V = \{$things beginning with c$\}$

$W = \{$things with six letters$\}$

$X = \{$things with four letters$\}$

D $V = \{12, 24, 36 \ldots 132, 144\}$

$M = \{48, 60, 24\}$ $N = \{72, 96, 120\}$ $O = \{35, 36\}$

$P = \{12, 48, 144\}$ $Q = \{90, 96, 108\}$ $R = \{84, 96\}$

Use the symbols $\subset$ or $\not\subset$ to make the following true.

$V \quad M, \quad P \quad V, \quad V \quad N, \quad Q \quad N, \quad O \quad N, \quad R \quad V.$

E $T = \{$A, B, C, D, E, F, G, H, I$\}$ $U = \{$J, K, L, M, N, O, P, A, E$\}$

$J = \{$letters in the word BEACH$\}$ $M = \{$letters in the word JOKE$\}$

$K = \{$letters in the word LUMP$\}$ $N = \{$letters in the word FACE$\}$

$L = \{$letters in the word BAND$\}$ $O = \{$letters in the word ONE$\}$

Use the symbols $\subset$ or $\not\subset$ to make the following true.

$J \quad T, \quad K \quad T, \quad K \quad U, \quad J \quad U, \quad L \quad T, \quad L \quad U, \quad N \quad T, \quad M \quad U, \quad O \quad U.$

Venn diagrams

A

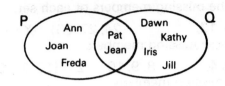

$P = \{$girls in the gym class$\}$

$Q = \{$girls in the ballet class$\}$

1 Which children like gym?

2 Which children like ballet?

3 Which children like both?

B 1 $M = \{$multiples of 3 between 1 and 31$\}$

$N = \{$multiples of 2 between 1 and 31$\}$

Draw the Venn diagram and say which numbers are in both sets.

2 $V = \{$letters in the word history$\}$

$W = \{$letters in the word geography$\}$

Draw the Venn diagram and say which letters are in both sets.

C 1

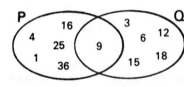

a Name set P.

b Name set Q.

Complete $P \cup Q = \{$ $\}$ and $P \cap Q = \{ \}$

2 $A = \{$numbers divisible by 5 less than 31$\}$

$B = \{$numbers divisible by 3 less than 31$\}$

Draw a Venn diagram of these sets and then complete

a $A \cup B = \{$ $\}$

b $A \cap B = \{$ $\}$

3 $X = \{$factors of 24$\}$

$Y = \{$factors of 50$\}$

Draw a Venn diagram of these sets and then complete

a $X \cup Y = \{$ $\}$

b $X \cap Y = \{$ $\}$